FUNDAMENTALS
OF GEOMETRY

THE ALLYN and BACON SERIES

Topics in Contemporary Mathematics

FUNDAMENTALS
OF
GEOMETRY

Howard Eves
Professor of Mathematics
University of Maine

ALLYN AND BACON, INC.   BOSTON

In memory of

Spofford Harris Kimball

gentleman, scholar, friend

PREFACE

There have been a number of requests, particularly from smaller colleges and teachers' colleges, that a concise, one-semester, inexpensive, first-course text, aimed chiefly at prospective and present teachers of high school geometry, be constructed from Volume One of my more massive *A Survey of Geometry* (Boston: Allyn and Bacon, Inc., 1963). The present work is an attempt to satisfy the above requests.

Here, briefly, are some of the features of the work.

1. *Geometric content.* It is an obvious truism that a teacher of high school geometry should know appreciably more about his subject than just the material he teaches. The additional information should be a sequel to, or extension of, that which he teaches, and should not (at least in a first course) run too far afield from the subject matter of his high school classes. Much of this material should be such that it can be passed on to a gifted or interested geometry student, and much of it should tend to knit together parts of the usual high school information. Also, it is wise generally to include material that has, in one form or another, entered into the mainstream of mathematics. These have been the guidelines for the selection of most of the geometric content of this book.

2. *Geometric concepts.* The two most significant, fruitful, and general concepts that can be introduced in an elementary course in geometry are the idea of a deductive chain of geometric statements and the idea of geometric transformation. Essentially each section of this work is an illustration of a deductive development

of some important and connected part of geometry, and the transform-solve-invert technique of transformation theory constitutes the red thread that runs through the entire work. It is the former of the two concepts that leads to the axiomatic foundation of geometry, and the latter that leads to the group-theoretic foundation of geometry. In a second-semester follow-up course, these two concepts should be more sharply pursued — introducing the student, on the one hand, to non-Euclidean geometry, axiomatics, finite and abstract geometries, and on the other hand to the Erlanger program and Klein's remarkable codification of geometries.

In addition to introducing the student to the above two principal concepts, a number of lesser concepts are exploited, such as those of directed elements, ideal elements, cross ratio, and duality.

3. *Richness of geometric attack.* The old saying, "There is more than one way to skin a cat," is certainly true in geometry: there is no unique way to prove a theorem or to solve a problem. To illustrate this, several important theorems have been selected and, as suitable methods have been introduced, they have been established in a number of different ways. Thus some key theorems, such as the Desargues two-triangle theorem and the Pascal mystic-hexagram theorem, appear and reappear as variations on a geometric theme.

4. *Underlying history.* It has quite properly been said that "no subject loses more than mathematics by any attempt to dissociate it from its history." The treatment in this book is strongly historical, for the study is concerned with some fundamental geometric ideas, and a real appreciation and understanding of ideas is possible only with an analysis of origins. The whole first chapter is historical, and each subsequent chapter and topic is introduced with historical comments. The history of a subject enlivens it, heightens its interest and appeal, and brings out the human element and certain valuable cultural links.

5. *Flexibility.* A certain flexibility in a text is desirable — so that the text can fit classes of different degrees of preparation, courses of various lengths, and the varying whims of the instructors. Following are some suggested uses of this text:

(a) For a short course: A quick reading of Chap. I followed by Chaps. II and III, possibly omitting some of the later sections of Chap. III.

(b) For a slow class: Chaps. I, II, III.

(c) For a normal class: Chaps. I, II, III, and IV or Chaps. I, II, III, and V.

(d) For better-prepared classes: A quick reading of Chap. I

followed by Chaps. II, III, IV, and V, possibly omitting some of the later sections of Chaps. IV and V.

6. *Problems.* It is difficult to overstate the importance of problems in mathematics in general and in geometry in particular. Problems are an integral part of geometry, for one *learns* geometry chiefly by *doing* geometry. This text contains an ample supply of problems, many of which introduce the student to interesting things not appearing in the text proper. The student will miss much if he does not dip into the problem material. Since geometry problems often present difficulties to a beginner, a collection of suggestions for solutions of most of the problems is given at the end of the work.

7. *Bibliography.* At the end of the book there also appears a short bibliography of other related works. Volume One of *A Survey of Geometry*, of which the present work is a condensation, offers more and fuller treatments of topics, many more problems, and a much more detailed bibliography.

The writing of this book, like so much of my recent work, was made possible by the understanding of my department chairman, Spofford Kimball. Just as I was finishing the manuscript, that remarkable, generous, kind, and able leader — that genuine friend — suddenly passed away. The void created can never, for me, quite be refilled.

CONTENTS

xi

I. THE FOUNTAINHEAD

This first chapter describes the source from which essentially all geometrical investigations of the modern era have arisen. This makes possible, in the succeeding chapters, an analysis of the origins of the fundamental ideas there introduced — an analysis without which a genuine appreciation of those ideas is not possible.

The chapter also serves as a review for the reader who has been too long away from his elementary geometry. Before discussing some of the advances of the modern era, the reader is given a chance to recall the basic concepts and terminology that were considered in his high school geometry course, and without which it would be rather foolhardy to proceed.

1.1   THE EARLIEST GEOMETRY

The first geometrical considerations of man are unquestionably very ancient, and would seem to have their origin in simple observations stemming from human ability to recognize physical form and to compare shapes and sizes.

There were innumerable circumstances in the life of even the most primitive man that would lead to a certain amount of sub-conscious geometric discovery. The notion of distance was undoubtedly one of the first geometrical concepts to be developed. The estimation of the time needed to make a journey led very early to the realization that the straight line constitutes the shortest path from one point to another; indeed, most animals seem instinctively to realize this. The need to bound land led to the notion of simple geometric figures, such as rectangles, squares, and triangles. In fact, it seems natural, when fencing a piece of land, first to fix the corners and then to join these by straight lines. Other simple geometrical concepts, such as those of vertical, parallel, and perpendicular, would have been suggested by the construction of walls and dwellings.

Many observations in the daily life of early man must have led to the conception of curves, surfaces, and solids. Instances of circles were numerous − for example, the periphery of the sun or the moon, the rainbow, the seed heads of many flowers, and the cross section of a log. A thrown stone describes a parabola; an unstretched cord hangs in a catenary curve; a wound rope lies in a spiral; spider webs illustrate regular polygons. The growth rings of a tree, the swelling circles caused by a pebble cast into a pond, and figures on certain shells suggest the idea of families of curves. Many fruits and pebbles are spherical, and bubbles on water are hemispherical; some bird eggs are approximately ellipsoids of revolution; a ring is a torus; tree trunks are circular cylinders; conical shapes are frequently seen in nature. Early potters made many surfaces and solids of revolution. The bodies of men and animals, most leaves and flowers, and certain shells and crystals illustrate the notion of symmetry. The idea of volume arises immediately in the consideration of receptacles to hold liquids and other simple commodities.

Examples like the above can be multiplied almost indefinitely. Physical forms which possess an ordered character, contrasting as they do with the haphazard and unorganized shapes of most bodies, necessarily attract the attention of even the least reflective mind − and some elementary geometric concepts are thereby brought to light. Such geometry may be called *subconscious geometry* . This subconscious geometry was employed by very early man in the making of decorative ornaments and patterns, and it is probably quite correct to say that early art did much to prepare the way for later geometric development. The evolution of subconscious geometry in little children is well known and easily observed.

Now, in the beginning, man considered only concrete geometrical problems, which presented themselves individually and with no observed interconnections. When human intelligence was able to extract from a set of concrete geometrical relationships a general abstract relationship containing the former as particular cases, geometry became a science. In this capacity, geometry has the advantage of ordering practical problems into sets such that the problems in a set can be solved by the same general procedure. One thus arrives at the notion of a geometrical law or rule. For example, comparing the lengths of circular courses with their diameters would lead, over a period of time, to the geometrical law that the ratio of circumference to diameter is a constant.

There is no evidence which permits us to estimate the number of centuries that passed before man was able to raise geometry to the status of a science, but all the writers of antiquity who concerned themselves with this matter unanimously agree upon the Nile valley of ancient Egypt as the place where subconscious geometry first became *scientific geometry*. The famous Greek historian Herodotus (*ca.* 485 B.C.-*ca.* 425 B.C.) has stated the thesis as follows:

> They said also that this king [Sesostris] divided the land among all Egyptians so as to give each one a quadrangle of equal size and to draw from each his revenues, by imposing a tax to be levied yearly. But every one from whose part the river tore away anything, had to go to him and notify what had happened. He then sent the overseers, who had to measure out by how much the land had become smaller, in order that the owner might pay on what was left, in proportion to the entire tax imposed. In this way, it appears to me, geometry originated, which passed thence to Hellas.

Thus the traditional account finds in early Egyptian surveying practices the beginnings of geometry as a science; indeed, the word "geometry" means "measurement of the earth." While we cannot be certain of this origin, it does seem safe to assume that scientific geometry arose from practical necessity, appearing several thousand years before our era in certain areas of the ancient orient as a science to assist in engineering, agriculture, business, and religious ritual. There is historical evidence that this occurred not only along the Nile River of Egypt, but also in other great river basins, such as the Tigris and Euphrates of Mesopotamia, the Indus and Ganges of south-central Asia, and the Hwang Ho and the Yangtze of eastern Asia. These river basins cradled advanced forms of society known for their engineering prowess in marsh drainage, irrigation, flood control, and the erection of great edifices and religious structures. Such projects required the development of much practical geometry.

1.2 THE EMPIRICAL NATURE OF PRE-HELLENIC GEOMETRY

As far back as history allows us to grope into the past, we still find present a sizeable body of material that can be called practical, or scientific, geometry.

The earliest existing records of man's activity in the field of geometry are some inscribed baked clay tablets unearthed in Mesopotamia and believed to date, in part at least, from Sumerian times of about 3000 B.C. There are other generous supplies of Babylonian tablets coming from later periods, such as the First Babylonian Dynasty of King Hammurabi's era, the New Babylonian Empire of Nebuchadnezzar, and the following Persian and Selucidan eras. From these tablets we see that ancient Babylonian geometry is intimately related to practical mensuration. Numerous concrete examples show that the Babylonians of 2000 to 1600 B.C. were familiar with the general rules for computing the area of a rectangle, the areas of right and isosceles triangles (and perhaps the general triangle), the area of the special trapezoid having one side perpendicular to the parallel sides, the volume of a rectangular parallelepiped, and, more generally, the volume of a right prism with special trapezoidal base. The circumference of a circle was frequently taken as three times the diameter, and the area as one-twelfth the square of the circumference (both correct for $\pi = 3$), and the volume of a right circular cylinder was then obtained by finding the product of the base and the altitude. The volume of a frustum of a cone or of a square pyramid appears incorrectly as the product of the altitude and half the sum of the bases. There also seems to be evidence that the ancient Babylonians used the incorrect formula

$$K = (a + c)(b + d)/4$$

for the area of a quadrilateral having a, b, c, d for consecutive sides. These peoples knew that corresponding sides of two similar right triangles are proportional, that the altitude through the vertex of an isosceles triangle bisects the base, and that an angle inscribed in a semicircle is a right angle. The Pythagorean Theorem was also known, even as far back as approximately 2000 B.C.

Our chief sources of information concerning ancient Egyptian geometry are the Moscow and Rhind papyri, mathematical texts containing 25 and 85 problems, respectively, and dating from approximately 1850 B.C. and 1650 B.C. There is also, in the Berlin Museum, the oldest extant astronomical or surveying instrument — a combination plumb line and sight rod — which comes from the ancient Egypt of about 1950 B.C. The Berlin Museum also possesses an Egyptian sundial dating from about 1500 B.C., and which is the oldest sundial in existence. These instruments reveal, of course, a knowledge at the times of some associated practical geometry. One should also point out that the great pyramid of Gizeh, whose very careful construction certainly involved some practical geometry, was erected about 2900 B.C.

Twenty-six of the 110 problems in the Moscow and Rhind papyri are geometric. Most of these problems stem from mensuration formulas needed for computation of land areas and granary volumes. The area of a circle is taken as equal to that of the square on 8/9 of the diameter, and the volume of a right cylinder as the product of the area of the base by the length of the altitude. Recent investigations seem to show that the ancient Egyptians knew that the area of any triangle is given by half the product of base and altitude. Some of the problems seem to concern themselves with the cotangent of the dihedral angle between the base and a face of a pyramid, and others show an acquaintance with the elementary theory of similar figures. Although there is no documentary evidence that the ancient Egyptians were aware of the Pythagorean Theorem, early Egyptian surveyors realized that a triangle having sides of lengths 3, 4, and 5 units is a right triangle. It is curious that the incorrect formula

$$K = (a + c)(b + d)/4$$

for the area of an arbitrary quadrilateral with successive sides of lengths a, b, c, d, appears in an inscription found in the tomb of Ptolemy XI, who died in 51 B.C.

Very remarkable is the existence in the Moscow papyrus of a numerical example of the correct formula for the volume of a frustum of a square pyramid,

$$V = h(a^2 + ab + b^2)/3,$$

where h is the altitude and a and b are the lengths of the sides of the two square bases. No other unquestionably genuine example of this formula has been found in pre-Hellenic mathematics, and since its proof demands some form of integral calculus, its discovery must certainly be regarded as an extraordinary piece of induction.

E. T. Bell has aptly referred to this early Egyptian achievement as "the greatest Egyptian pyramid."

Very likely, mathematical accomplishments similar to those of ancient Egypt and Babylonia also occurred in ancient India and China, but we know very little indeed with any degree of certainty about those accomplishments. The ancient Egyptians recorded their work on stone and papyrus, the latter fortunately resisting the ages because of Egypt's unusually dry climate, and the Babylonians used imperishable baked clay tablets. In contrast to the use of these media, the early Indians and Chinese used very perishable writing materials such as bark bast and bamboo. Thus it has come to pass that we have a fair quantity of definite information, obtained from primary sources, about the mathematics of ancient Egypt and Babylonia, while we know very little about the study in ancient India and China.

It is interesting to note that in all pre-Hellenic mathematics we do not find a single instance of what we today call a logical demonstration. In place of a general argument there is merely a step-by-step description of some process applied to particular numerical cases. Beyond some very simple considerations, the mathematical relations employed by the early Egyptians and Babylonians resulted essentially from "trial-and-error" methods, with the result that many of their formulas are incorrect. In other words, pre-Hellenic mathematics was little more than a practically workable empiricism — a collection of rule-of-thumb procedures that gave results of sufficient acceptability for the simple needs of those early civilizations. Mathematics, and geometry in particular, appears as a laboratory study.

Empirical reasoning may be described as the formulation of conclusions based upon experience and observation; no real understanding is involved, and the logical element does not appear. Empirical reasoning often entails stodgy fiddling with special cases, observation of coincidences and the frequent employment of analogy, experience at good guessing, considerable experimentation, and flashes of intuition.

In spite of the empirical nature of pre-Hellenic mathematics, with its complete neglect of proof and the seemingly little attention paid to the difference between exact and approximate truth, one is nevertheless struck by the extent and diversity of the problems successfully attacked. Apparently a great deal of elementary mathematical truth can be discovered by empirical methods when supplemented by extensive experimentation carried on patiently over a long period of time.

PROBLEMS

1.2-1   Show that the ancient Babylonian formula

$$K = (a + c)(b + d)/4,$$

for the area of a quadrilateral having a, b, c, d for consecutive sides, gives too large an answer for all nonrectangular quadrilaterals.

1.2-2   Interpret the following, found on a Babylonian tablet believed to date from about 2600 B.C.:

"60 is the circumference, 2 is the perpendicular, find the chord."
"Thou, double 2 and get 4, dost thou not see? Take 4 from 20, thou gettest 16. Square 20, thou gettest 400. Square 16, thou gettest 256. Take 256 from 400, thou gettest 144. Find the square root of 144. 12, the square root, is the chord. Such is the procedure."

1.2-3   In the Rhind papyrus the area of a circle is taken as equal to that of a square on 8/9 of the circle's diameter. Show that this is equivalent to taking $\pi = (4/3)^4 = 3.1604\cdots$.

1.2-4   Solve the following two problems found in the Moscow papyrus:
(a)   The area of a rectangle is 12, and the width is 3/4 of the length, what are the dimensions?
(b)   One leg of a right triangle is 2-1/2 times the other, the area is 20, what are the dimensions?

1.2-5   (a)   In the Moscow papyrus we find the following numerical example: "If you are told: A truncated pyramid of 6 for the vertical height by 4 on the base by 2 on the top. You are to square this 4, result 16. You are to double 4, result 8. You are to square 2, result 4. You are to add the 16, the 8, and the 4, result 28. You are to take one third of 6, result 2. You are to take 28 twice, result 56. See, it is 56. You will find it right."
Show that this illustrates the general formula

$$V = h(a^2 + ab + b^2)/3,$$

giving the volume of a frustum of a square pyramid in terms of the height h and the sides a and b of the bases. (This problem has been called "the greatest Egyptian pyramid.")

(b) Assuming the familiar formula for the volume of any pyramid (volume equals one-third the product of base and altitude), show that the volume of a frustum of a pyramid is given by the product of the height of the frustum and the heronian mean of the bases of the frustum. (If m and n are two positive numbers, then $H = (m + \sqrt{mn} + n)/3$ is called the *heronian mean* of the two numbers.)

1.2-6 The *Śulvasūtras*, ancient Hindu religious writings dating from about 500 B.C., are of interest in the history of mathematics because they embody certain geometrical rules for the construction of altars that show an acquaintance with the Pythagorean Theorem. Among the rules furnished there appear empirical solutions of the circle-squaring problem which are equivalent to taking $d = (2 + \sqrt{2})s/3$ and $s = 13d/15$, where d is the diameter of the circle and s is the side of the equivalent square. These formulas are equivalent to taking what values for π?

1.2-7 The Hindu mathematician Āryabhata wrote early in the sixth century A.D. His work is a poem of 33 couplets called the *Ganita*. Following are translations of two of the couplets:

(1) The area of a triangle is the product of the altitude and half the base; half of the product of this area and the height is the volume of the solid of six edges.

(2) Half the circumference multiplied by half the diameter gives the area of the circle; this area multiplied by its own square root gives the volume of the sphere.

Show that, in each of these couplets, Āryabhata is correct in two dimensions but wrong in three. We note that Hindu mathematics remained empirical long after the Greeks had introduced the deductive feature.

1.2-8 (a) An early Chinese work, dating probably from the second century B.C., which had considerable influence on the development of mathematics in China was the *K'ui-ch'ang Suan-Shu*, or *Arithmetic in Nine Sections*. In this work we find the formula $s(c + s)/2$ for the area of a circular segment of chord c and depth s. Show how this formula might have been obtained empirically and obtain a correct formula in terms of these quantities.

(b)   Solve the following problem found in the Chinese *Arithmetic in Nine Sections:*
There grows in the middle of a circular pond 10 feet in diameter a reed which projects one foot out of the water. When it is drawn down it just reaches the edge of the pond. How deep is the water?

1.2-9 (a)   There are reports that ancient Egyptian surveyors laid out right angles by constructing 3–4–5 triangles with a rope divided into 12 equal parts by 11 knots. Show how this can be done.

(b)   Since there is no documentary evidence to the effect that the Egyptians were aware of even a particular case of the Pythagorean Theorem, the following purely academic problem arises: Show, without using the Pythagorean Theorem, its converse, or any of its consequences, that the 3–4–5 triangle is a right triangle. Solve this problem by means of Fig. 1.2a, which appears in the *Chóu-pei,* the oldest known Chinese mathematical work, which may date back to the second millennium B.C.

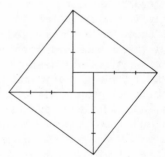

FIG. 1.2a

1.3   THE GREEK CONTRIBUTION OF AXIOMATICS

The economic and political changes of the last centuries of the second millennium B.C. caused the power of Egypt and Babylonia to wane, new peoples came to the fore, and it happened that the further development of geometry passed over to the Greeks. The extent of the debt of Greek geometry to ancient oriental geometry is difficult to estimate, nor is the path of transmission from the one to the other yet satisfactorily uncovered. That the debt is considerably greater than was formerly believed has become evident with the twentieth-century researches on Babylonian and Egyptian records. Early Greek writers themselves expressed respect for the wisdom of the East, and this wisdom was available to anyone who could travel to Egypt and Babylonia.

But, whatever the strength of the historical connection between Greek and ancient oriental geometry, the Greeks transformed the subject into something vastly different from the set of empirical conclusions worked out by their predecessors. The Greeks insisted that geometric fact must be established, not by empirical procedures, but by deductive reasoning; geometrical conclusions must be arrived at by logical demonstration rather than by trial-and-error experimentation. Geometrical truth is to be attained in the study room rather than in the laboratory. In short, the Greeks transformed the empirical, or scientific, geometry of the ancient Egyptians and Babylonians into what we might call *deductive*, or *demonstrative, geometry*.

It is disappointing that, unlike the study of ancient Egyptian and Babylonian geometry, there exist virtually no primary sources for the study of early Greek geometry. We are forced to rely upon manuscripts and accounts that are dated several hundred years after the original treatments had been written. In spite of this situation, however, scholars of classicism have been able to build up a rather consistent, though somewhat hypothetical, account of the history of early Greek geometry.

Our principal source of information concerning very early Greek geometry is the so-called *Eudemian Summary* of Proclus. This summary constitutes a few pages of Proclus' *Commentary on Euclid, Book I,* and is a very brief outline of the development of Greek geometry from the earliest times to Euclid. Although Proclus lived in the fifth century A.D., a good thousand years after the inception of Greek geometry, he still had access to a number of historical and critical works which are now lost to us except for the fragments and allusions preserved by him and others. Among these lost works is what was apparently a full history of Greek geometry, covering the period prior to 335 B.C., written by Eudemus, a pupil of Aristotle. The *Eudemian Summary* is so named because it is admittedly based upon this earlier work.

According to the *Eudemian Summary,* Greek geometry appears to have started in an essential way with the work of Thales of Miletus in the first half of the sixth century B.C. This versatile genius, declared to be one of the "seven wise men" of antiquity, was a worthy founder of systematic geometry, and is the first known individual with whom the use of deductive methods in geometry is associated. Thales, the summary tells us, sojourned for a time in Egypt and brought geometry back with him to Greece, where he began to apply to the subject the deductive procedures of Greek philosophy. He is credited with a number of very elementary geometrical results, the value of which is not to be measured by their content but rather by the belief that he supported them with a certain amount of logical reasoning instead of intuition and experiment.

The next outstanding Greek mathematician mentioned in the *Eudemian Summary* is Pythagoras, who is claimed to have continued the systematization of geometry that was begun some fifty years earlier by Thales. Pythagoras was born about 572 B.C., on the island of Samos, one of the Aegian islands near Thales' home city of Miletus, and it is quite possible that he studied under the older man. It seems that Pythagoras then visited Egypt and perhaps traveled even more extensively about the ancient orient. When, on returning home, he found Ionia under Persian dominion, he decided to migrate to the Greek seaport of Crotona in southern Italy. Here he founded the celebrated Pythagorean school, a brotherhood knit together with secret and cabalistic rites and observances, and committed to the study of philosophy, mathematics, and natural science.

In spite of the mystical nature of much of Pythagorean study, the members of the society contributed, during the two hundred or so years following the founding of their organization, a good deal of sound mathematics. Thus, in geometry, they developed the properties of parallel lines and used them to prove that the sum of the angles of any triangle is equal to two right angles. They contributed in a noteworthy manner to Greek geometrical algebra, and they developed a fairly complete theory of proportion, though it was limited only to commensurable magnitudes, and used it to deduce properties of similar figures. They were aware of the existence of at least three of the regular polyhedral solids, and they discovered the incommensurability of a side and a diagonal of a square. Although much of this information was already known to the Babylonians of earlier times, the deductive aspect of mathematics is thought to have been considerably exploited and advanced in this work of the Pythagoreans. Chains of propositions in which successive propositions were derived from earlier ones in the chain began to emerge. As the chains lengthened, and some were tied to others, the bold idea of developing all of geometry in one long chain suggested itself. It is claimed in the *Eudemian Summary* that a Pythagorean, Hippocrates of Chios, was the first to attempt, with at least partial success, a logical presentation of geometry in the form of a single chain of propositions based upon a few initial definitions and assumptions. Improved attempts were made by Leon, Theudius, and others. And then, about 300 B.C., Euclid produced his epoch-making effort, the *Elements* , a single deductive chain of 465 propositions neatly and beautifully comprising plane and solid geometry, number theory, and Greek geometrical algebra. From its very first appearance this work was accorded the highest respect, and it so quickly and so completely superseded all previous efforts of the same nature that now no trace remains of the earlier efforts. The effect of this single work on the future development of geometry has been immense and is difficult to overstate. In the next section we shall consider in some detail the contents of this magnificent work; in the remainder of this section we comment on its remarkable form.

At some time between Thales in 600 B.C. and Euclid in 300 B.C. was developed the notion of a logical discourse as a sequence of statements obtained by deductive reasoning from a set of initial statements assumed at the outset of the discourse. Certainly, if one is going to present an argument by deductive procedure, any statement of the argument will have to be derived from some previous statement or statements of the argument, and such a previous statement must itself be derived from some still more previous statement or statements. Clearly this cannot be continued backward indefinitely, nor should one resort to illogical circularity by deriving a statement B from a statement A, and then later deriving statement A from statement B. The only way out of the difficulty is to set down, toward the start of the argument, a collection of primary statements which are to be accepted by the reader, and then to proceed, purely by deductive reasoning, to derive all the other statements of the discourse. Now both the primary and derived statements of the discourse are statements about the technical matter of the discourse, and hence involve special or technical terms. These terms need to be defined. Since technical terms must be defined by means of other technical terms, and these other technical terms by means of still others, one is faced with a difficulty similar to that encountered with the statements of the discourse. In order to get started, and to avoid circularity of definition where term y is defined by means of term x, and then later term x by means of term y, one is forced to decide at the very start of the discourse upon a collection of basic technical terms which will receive no definition except that implicitly given to them by the primary statements of the discourse. All subsequent technical terms of the discourse must be defined explicitly by means of previous technical terms of the discourse.

An argument which is carried out according to the above plan is said to be developed by *axiomatics*. Certainly one of the most outstanding contributions of the early Greeks to mathematics was the formulation of an early aspect of axiomatics and the insistence that mathematics be systematized by this procedure. Euclid's *Elements* is the earliest extensively developed example of the use of axiomatics that has come down to us.

Today we refer to the primary undefined terms as the *primitive terms* of the discourse, the primary unproved statements as the *postulates* (or *axioms)* of the discourse, and the deduced statements as the *theorems* of the discourse.

PROBLEMS

1.3-1   There are two versions of how Thales, when in Egypt, evoked admiration by calculating the height of a pyramid by shadows. The earlier account, given by Hieronymus, a pupil of Aristotle, says that Thales determined the height of the pyramid by measuring the shadow it cast at the moment a man's shadow was equal to his height. The later version, given by Plutarch, says that he set up a stick and then made use of similar triangles. Both versions fail to mention the difficulty, in either case, of obtaining the length of the shadow of the pyramid — that is, the distance from the apex of the shadow to the center of the base of the pyramid.

Devise a method, based on similar triangles and independent of latitude and time of year, for determining the height of a pyramid *from two shadow observations*.

1.3-2 (a)   Tradition is unanimous in ascribing to Pythagoras the independent discovery of the theorem on the right triangle which now universally bears his name — that the square on the hypotenuse of a right triangle is equal to the sum of the squares on the legs. We have noted that this theorem was known to the Babylonians of Hammurabi's time, over a thousand years earlier, but the first general proof of the theorem may have been given by Pythagoras. There has been much conjecture as to the proof Pythagoras might have offered, and it is generally felt that it probably was a dissection type of proof such as is suggested by Fig. 1.3a. Supply the proof.

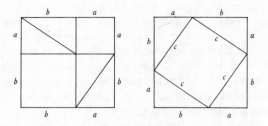

FIG. 1.3a

(Since Pythagoras' times, many different proofs of the Pythagorean Theorem have been supplied. In the second edition of his book *The Pythagorean Proposition*, E. S. Loomis has collected and classified 370 demonstrations of this famous theorem.)
(b) State and prove the converse of the Pythagorean Theorem.

1.3-3 Show that there can be no more than five regular polyhedra.

1.3-4 (a) Prove that $\sqrt{2}$ is not a rational number.
(b) Show that a side and a diagonal of a square are incommensurable (that is, have no common unit of measure).
(c) Prove that the straight line through the points (0,0) and $(1, \sqrt{2})$ of a rectangular Cartesian coordinate system passes through no point, other than (0,0), of the coordinate lattice.
(d) Show how the coordinate lattice may be used to find rational approximations of $\sqrt{2}$.

1.3-5 Assuming the equality of alternate interior angles formed by a transversal cutting a pair of parallel lines, prove the following:
(a) The sum of the angles of a triangle is equal to a straight angle.
(b) The sum of the interior angles of a convex polygon of n sides is equal to $n - 2$ straight angles.

1.3-6 Assuming that the area of a rectangle is given by the product of its two dimensions, establish the following chain of theorems:
(a) The area of a parallelogram is equal to the product of its base and altitude.

(b)   The area of a triangle is equal to half the product of any side and the altitude on that side.

(c)   The area of a right triangle is equal to half the product of its two legs.

(d)   The area of a triangle is equal to half the product of its perimeter and the radius of its inscribed circle.

(e)   The area of a trapezoid is equal to the product of its altitude and half the sum of its bases.

(f)   The area of a regular polygon is equal to half the product of its perimeter and its apothem.

(g)   The area of a circle is equal to half the product of its circumference and its radius.

1.3-7   As a simple example of a discourse conducted by axiomatics, consider the following postulate set in which *abba* and *dabba* are primitive terms:

POSTULATE 1.   *Each dabba is a nonempty collection of abbas.*

POSTULATE 2.   *Each abba belongs to at least one dabba.*

POSTULATE 3.   *For each pair of abbas there is one and only one dabba to which both belong.*

DEFINITION.   Two dabbas having no members in common are called *conjugate dabbas.*

POSTULATE 4.   *For each dabba there is one and only one conjugate dabba.*

From these postulates deduce the following theorems:

THEOREM 1.   *Each abba is a member of at least two dabbas.*

THEOREM 2.   *Each dabba contains at least two abbas.*

THEOREM 3.   *There exist at least four abbas.*

1.4   EUCLID'S *ELEMENTS*

Whoever even casually pages through a copy of Euclid's *Elements* is bound to realize that, notwithstanding certain imperfections, he is examining one of the foremost works ever compiled. This treatise by Euclid is rightfully regarded as the first great landmark in the history of mathematical thought and organization. No work, except the Bible, has been more widely used, edited, or studied. For more than two millennia it has dominated all teaching of geometry, and over a thousand editions of it have appeared since the first one printed in 1482. As the prototype of the axiomatic method, its impact on the development of mathematics has been enormous, and a surprising number of important subsequent developments in geometry owe their origin and inspiration to some part or feature of this great work.

It is no detraction that Euclid's work is largely a compilation of works of predecessors, for its chief merit lies precisely in the consummate skill with which the propositions were selected and arranged in a logical sequence presumably following from a small handful of initial assumptions. Nor is it a detraction that the search-light of modern criticism has revealed certain defects in the structure of the work; it would be very remarkable indeed if such an early and colossal attempt by the axiomatic method should be free of blemishes.

No copy of Euclid's *Elements* actually dating from the author's time has been found. The modern editions of the *Elements* are based upon a revision prepared by Theon of Alexandria almost 700 years after the original work had been written. It was not until the beginning of the nineteenth century that an older copy, showing only minor differences from Theon's recension, was discovered in the Vatican library. A careful study of citations and commentary by early writers indicates that the initial definitions, axioms, and postulates of the original treatise differed some from the revisions, but that the propositions and their proofs have largely remained as Euclid wrote them.

In the thirteen books that comprise Euclid's *Elements* there is a total of 465 propositions. Contrary to popular impression, many of these propositions are concerned, not with geometry, but with number theory and with Greek (geometrical) algebra.

Book I commences, of course, with the necessary preliminary definitions, postulates, and axioms. Though today mathematicians use the words "axiom" and "postulate" synonymously, some of the early Greeks made a distinction, the distinction adopted by Euclid perhaps being that an axiom is an initial assumption common to all studies, whereas a postulate is an initial assumption pertaining to the study at hand. The 48 propositions of Book I fall into three groups. The first 26 deal mainly with properties of triangles and include the three well-known congruence theorems. Propositions I 27* through I 32 establish the theory of parallels and prove that the sum of the angles of a triangle is equal to two right angles. The remaining propositions of the book deal with parallelograms, triangles, and squares, with special reference to area relations. Proposition I 47 is the Pythagorean Theorem, and the final proposition, I 48, is the converse of the Pythagorean Theorem.

*By I 27 is meant Proposition 27 of Book I.

The material of this book was developed by the early Pythagoreans.

Book II deals with the transformation of areas and the Greek geometrical algebra of the Pythagorean school. It is in this book that we find the geometrical equivalents of a number of algebraic identities. At the end of the book are two propositions which establish the generalization of the Pythagorean Theorem that we today refer to as the "law of cosines."

Book III contains those familiar theorems about circles, chords, tangents, and the measurement of associated angles which we find in our high school geometry texts.

In Book IV are found discussions of the Pythagorean constructions, with straightedge and compasses, of regular polygons of three, four, five, six, and fifteen sides.

Book V gives a masterly exposition of the theory of proportion as originated by Eudoxus. It was this theory, which is applicable to incommensurable as well as commensurable magnitudes, that resolved a "logical scandal" created by the Pythagorean discovery of irrational numbers. Prior to the discovery of irrational numbers it was intuitively felt that any two line segments are commensurable, and the Pythagorean treatment of proportion was built on this false premise. The Eudoxian theory of proportion later provided a foundation, developed by Richard Dedekind in the late nineteenth century, for the real-number system of analysis. Present-day high school geometry texts do not employ the Eudoxian theory, but rather the earlier Pythagorean theory completed by some elementary limit theory.

Book VI applies the Eudoxian theory of proportion to plane geometry. Here we find the fundamental theorems on similar triangles and constructions giving third, fourth, and mean proportionals. We also find a geometrical solution of quadratic equations, and the proposition that the internal bisector of an angle of a triangle divides the opposite side into segments proportional to the other two sides. There probably is no theorem in this book that was not known to the early Pythagoreans, but the pre-Eudoxian proofs of many of them were at fault since they were based upon an incomplete theory of proportion.

Books VII, VIII, and IX, containing a total of 102 propositions, deal with elementary number theory. In these books are many beautiful theorems about the natural numbers, but, since we are here concerned only with geometry, we forego any discussion of them.

Book X deals with irrationals, that is, with line segments which are incommensurable with respect to some given line segment.

Many scholars regard this book as perhaps the most remarkable in the *Elements*. Much of the subject matter of this book is believed due to Theaetetus, but the extraordinary completeness, elaborate classification, and finish are usually credited to Euclid. It taxes one's credulity to realize that the results of this book were arrived at by rhetorical reasoning unassisted by any convenient algebraic notation.

The remaining three books, XI, XII, and XIII, concern themselves with solid geometry, covering most of the material, with the exception of much of that on spheres, commonly found in high school texts today. The definitions, the theorems about lines and planes in space, and theorems concerning parallelepipeds are found in Book XI. Volumes are cleverly treated in Book XII, and constructions of the five regular polyhedra are given in Book XIII.

The traditional American high school texts in plane and solid geometry contain material on rectilinear figures, circles, proportion and similar figures, regular polygons, lines and planes in space, volumes of solids, and the sphere. Except for most of the work on spheres, this is largely the material of Euclid's Books I, III, IV, VI, XI, and XII. The material in current high school texts concerning the measurement of the circle and the sphere, and the material dealing with spherical triangles, is of later origin and is not found in the *Elements*.

PROBLEMS

1.4-1 By the "elements" of a deductive study the Greeks meant the leading, or key, theorems which are of wide and general use in the subject. Their function has been compared to that of the letters of the alphabet in relation to language; as a matter of fact, letters are called by the same name in Greek. The selection of the theorems to be taken as the elements of the subject requires the exercise of some judgment. If you were to choose two of the following theorems for "elements" of a course in plane geometry, which would you choose?

(1) The three altitudes of a triangle, produced if necessary, meet in a point.

(2) The sum of the three angles of a triangle is equal to two right angles.

(3) An angle inscribed in a circle is measured by half its intercepted arc.

(4) The tangents drawn from any point on the common chord

produced of two given intersecting circles are equal in length.

1.4-2 A geometry teacher is going to present the topic of parallelograms to her class. After defining *parallelogram*, what theorems about parallelograms should the teacher offer as the "elements" of the subject?

1.4-3 Preparatory to teaching the topic on similar figures, a geometry teacher gives a lesson or two on the theory of proportion. What theorems should she select for the "elements" of the treatment, and in what order should she arrange them?

1.4-4 Consider the following four statements, called, respectively, the *direct* statement, the *converse* statement, the *inverse* statement, and the *contrapositive* statement: (1) All a are b. (2) All b are a. (3) All non-a are non-b. (4) All non-b are non-a.
(a) Show that the direct and contrapositive statements are equivalent.
(b) Show that the converse and inverse statements are equivalent.
(c) Taking "All parallelograms are quadrilaterals" as the direct statement, give the converse, inverse, and contrapositive statements.

1.4-5 (a) Prove the theorem: *If a triangle is isosceles, then the bisectors of its base angles are equal.*
(b) Try to prove the converse of the theorem in part (a). (This converse is known as the *Steiner-Lehmus Theorem* and is not so easy to establish.)

1.4-6 Show that the "law of cosines" is a generalization of the Pythagorean Theorem.

1.4-7 Indicate how each of the following algebraic identities might be established geometrically, assuming that a, b, c, d are positive quantities.
(a) $(a + b)^2 = a^2 + 2ab + b^2$
(b) $(a - b)^2 = a^2 - 2ab + b^2$, $a > b$
(c) $a^2 - b^2 = (a + b)(a - b)$, $a > b$
(d) $a(b + c) = ab + ac$
(e) $(a + b)^2 = (a - b)^2 + 4ab$, $a > b$
(f) $(a + b)(c + d) = ac + bc + ad + bd$

1.4-8 (a) Let r and s denote the roots of the quadratic equation

$$x^2 - px + q^2 = 0,$$

where p and q are positive numbers. Show that $r + s = p$, $rs = q^2$, and r and s are both positive if $q \leqq p/2$.

(b) To solve the quadratic equation of part (a) geometrically for real roots, we must find line segments r and s from given line segments p and q. That is, we must construct a rectangle equivalent to a given square and having the sum of its base and altitude equal to a given line segment. Devise a suitable construction based on Fig. 1.4a, and show geometrically that for real roots to exist we must have $q \leqq p/2$.

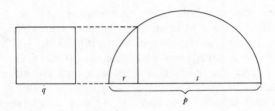

FIG. 1.4a

(c) Let r and s denote the roots of the quadratic equation

$$x^2 - px - q^2 = 0,$$

where p and q are positive numbers. Show that $r + s = p$, $rs = -q^2$, the roots are real, and the numerically larger one is positive while the other is negative.

(d) To solve the quadratic equation of part (c) geometrically, we must find line segments r and s from given line segments p and q. That is, we must construct a rectangle equivalent to a given square and having the difference of its base and altitude equal to a given line segment. Devise a suitable construction based on Fig. 1.4b (see facing page).

(e) Devise constructions for geometrically solving for real roots the quadratic equations $x^2 + px + q^2 = 0$ and $x^2 + px - q^2 = 0$, where p and q are positive numbers.

(f) Given a unit segment, geometrically solve the quadratic equation

$$x^2 - 7x + 12 = 0.$$

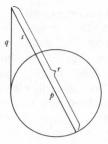

FIG. 1.4b

(g) Given a unit segment, geometrically solve the quadratic
     equation

$$x^2 + 4x - 21 = 0.$$

(h) With straightedge and compass, divide a segment m into
     two parts such that the difference of their squares shall be
     equal to their product.

(i) Show that, in part (h), the longer segment is a mean propor-
     tional between the shorter segment and the whole segment.
     (The line segment is said to be divided in *extreme and mean ratio,*
     or in *golden section.*)

1.5   THE CONTENT OF GREEK GEOMETRY

Euclid, Archimedes, and Apollonius mark the apogee of Greek
geometry, and it is no exaggeration to say that almost every
significant subsequent geometrical development, right up to and
including the present time, finds its origin in some work of
these three great scholars.

Very little is known about the life of Euclid beyond the fact
that he was the first professor of mathematics at the famed
University of Alexandria, and the father of the illustrious and long-
lived Alexandrian School of Mathematics. Even the dates of his
life and his birthplace are not known, but it seems probable that
he received his mathematical training in the Platonic school at
Athens.

Though Euclid's *Elements* is by far his most influential work,
indeed the most influential single work in geometry in the entire
history of the subject, he did write several other geometrical

treatises, some of which have survived to the present day. One of the latter, entitled the *Data*, is concerned with material of the first six books of the *Elements* . A *datum* may be defined as a set of parts of a figure such that if all but one are given, then that remaining one is determined. Thus the parts A, a, R of a triangle, where A is one angle, a the opposite side, and R the circumradius, constitute a datum, for, given any two of these parts, the third is thereby determined. This is clear either geometrically or from the relation $a = 2R \sin A$. It is apparent that a collection of data of this sort could be useful in the analysis which precedes the discovery of a construction or a proof, and this is undoubtedly the purpose of the work.

Another work in geometry by Euclid, which has come down to us through an Arabian translation, is the book *On Divisions*. Here we find construction problems requiring the division of a figure by a restricted straight line so that the parts will have areas in a prescribed ratio. An example is the problem of dividing a given triangle into two equal areas by a line drawn through a given point in the plane of the triangle.

Other geometrical works of Euclid that are now lost to us, and are known only from later commentaries, are the *Pseudaria*, or book of geometrical fallacies, *Porisms*, a relatively deep work about which there has been considerable speculation, *Conics*, a treatise in four books which was later completed and then added to by Apollonius, and *Surface Loci*, perhaps a treatise on surfaces of double curvature but about which nothing really certain is known. These works tend to show that Euclid delved considerably deeper into geometry than just the material of the *Elements*.

Euclid's other works concern applied mathematics, and two of these are extant: the *Phaenomena*, dealing with the spherical geometry required for observational astronomy, and the *Optics*, an elementary treatise on perspective. Euclid is supposed also to have written a work on the *Elements of Music*.

One of the very greatest mathematicians of all time, and certainly the greatest of antiquity, was Archimedes, a native of the Greek city of Syracuse on the island of Sicily. He was born about 287 B.C. and died during the Roman pillage of Syracuse in 212 B.C. There is a report that he spent time in Egypt, in all likelihood at the University of Alexandria, for he numbered among his friends Conon, Dositheus, and Eratosthenes; the first two were successors of Euclid, the last was a librarian, at the University. Many of Archimedes' mathematical discoveries were communicated in letters to these men.

The works of Archimedes are not compilations of achievements of predecessors, but are highly original creations. They are masterpieces of mathematical exposition and resemble to a remarkable extent, because of their high finish, economy of presentation, and rigor in demonstration, the articles found in present-day research journals. Some ten treatises have come down to us and there are various traces of lost works. Probably the most important contribution made to mathematics in these works is Archimedes' anticipation of some of the methods of the integral calculus.

Three of Archimedes' extant works are devoted to plane geometry. They are *Measurement of a Circle, Quadrature of the Parabola,* and *On Spirals.* It was in the first of these that Archimedes inaugurated the classical method of computing π. To simplify matters, suppose that we choose a circle with unit diameter. Then the length of the circumference of the circle is π. Now the length of the circumference of a circle lies between the perimeter of any inscribed polygon and that of any circumscribed polygon. Since it is a simple matter to compute the perimeters of the regular inscribed and circumscribed six-sided polygons, we easily obtain bounds for π. Now there are formulas which tell us how, from the perimeters of given regular inscribed and circumscribed polygons, we may obtain the perimeters of the regular inscribed and circumscribed polygons having twice the number of sides. By successive applications of this process, starting with the regular inscribed and circumscribed six-sided polygons, we can compute the perimeters of the regular inscribed and circumscribed polygons of 12, 24, 48, and 96 sides, in this way obtaining ever closer bounds for π. This is essentially what Archimedes did, finally obtaining the fact that π lies between 223/71 and 22/7, or that, to two decimal places, π is given by 3.14. This procedure of Archimedes was the start in the long history of securing ever more accurate approximations for the number π, reaching in 1967 the fantastic accuracy of 500,000 decimal places.

In the *Quadrature of the Parabola,* which contains 24 propositions, it is shown that the area of a parabolic segment is 4/3 that of the inscribed triangle having the same base and having its opposite vertex at the point where the tangent is parallel to the base. The summation of a convergent geometric series is involved. The work *On Spirals* contains 28 propositions devoted to properties of the curve which is now known as the spiral of Archimedes. In particular, the area enclosed by the curve and two radii vectors is found essentially as would be done today as a calculus exercise.

There are allusions to lost works on plane geometry by Archimedes, and there is reason to believe that some of the theorems
of these works have been preserved in the *Liber assumptorum* or
Book of Lemmas, a collection which has reached us through the
Arabic. One Arabian writer claims that Archimedes was the
discoverer of the celebrated formula

$$K = \sqrt{s(s - a)(s - b)(s - c)}$$

for the area of a triangle in terms of its three sides. This formula
is found in a later work of Heron of Alexandria.

Two of Archimedes' extant works are devoted to geometry of
three dimensions, namely, *On the Sphere and Cylinder* and *On Conoids
and Spheroids*. In the first of these, written in two books and
containing a total of 60 propositions, appear theorems giving the
areas of a sphere and of a zone of one base and volumes of a
sphere and of a segment of one base. In Book II appears the problem
of dividing a sphere by a plane into two segments whose volumes
shall be in a given ratio. This problem leads to a cubic equation
whose solution is not given in the text as it has come down to us,
but was found by Eutocius in an Archimedean fragment. There is
a discussion concerning the conditions under which the cubic
may have a real and positive root. Similar considerations do not
appear again in mathematics for over a thousand years. The treatise
On Conoids and Spheroids contains 40 propositions, which are concerned chiefly with an investigation of the volumes of quadrics of
revolution. In this work we find a derivation of the formula $A = \pi ab$
for the area of an ellipse having semiaxes a and b. Pappus has
ascribed to Archimedes 13 semiregular polyhedra, but unfortunately
Archimedes' own account of them is lost.[†]

There are two extant treatises by Archimedes on applied
mathematics, *On the Equilibrium of Planes* and *On Floating Bodies*. It
is interesting that in these works on mechanics, Archimedes
employed the axiomatic method. The physical postulates that must
be assumed in addition to the axioms and postulates of geometry
are first laid down, and the properties then carefully deduced.
It was not until the sixteenth-century work of Simon Stevin that
the science of statics and the theory of hydrostatics were appreciably
advanced beyond the points reached by Archimedes.

[†]Construction patterns for the Archimedean solids, and for many other polyhedral solids, can be
found in Miles C. Hartley, *Patterns of Polyhedra*, rev. ed. (Ann Arbor, Mich.: Edwards Brothers,
1957.)

Archimedes wrote two related essays on arithmetic, but these, being foreign to geometry, will not be considered here.

One of the most thrilling discoveries of modern times in the history of mathematics was the discovery by Heiberg, in Constantinople, as late as 1906, of Archimedes' long-lost treatise entitled *Method* . This work is in the form of a letter addressed to Eratosthenes and is important because of the information it furnishes concerning a "method" which Archimedes used to discover many of his theorems. Although the "method" can today be made rigorous by modern integration processes of the calculus, Archimedes used the "method" only to discover results, which he then established rigorously by his extension of the Eudoxian method of exhaustion.

The third mathematical giant of Greek antiquity was Apollonius, who was born about 262 B.C. in Perga in southern Asia Minor. As a young man he went to Alexandria, studied under the successors of Euclid, and then spent most of the remainder of his life at the University. He died somewhere around 200 B.C.

Although Apollonius was an astronomer of note and although he wrote on a variety of mathematical subjects, his chief bid to fame rests on his extraordinary and monumental *Conic Sections*, a work which earned him the title, among his contemporaries, of the "Great Geometer." Apollonius' *Conic Sections*, in eight books and containing about 400 propositions, is a thorough investigation of these curves, and completely superseded all earlier works on the subject. Only the first seven of the eight books have come down to us, the first four in Greek and the following three from a ninth-century Arabic translation. The first four books, of which I, II, and III are presumably founded on Euclid's earlier effort, deal with the general elementary theory of conics, while the later books are devoted to more specialized investigations.

Prior to Apollonius, the Greeks derived the conic sections from three types of cones of revolution, according as the vertex angle of the cone was less than, equal to, or greater than a right angle. By cutting each of three such cones with a plane perpendicular to an element of the cone an ellipse, parabola, and hyperbola respectively result (only one branch of the hyperbola appearing). Apollonius, on the other hand, in Book I of his treatise, obtains all the conic sections in the now familiar way from *one* arbitrary right or oblique circular *double* cone.

Pappus has given brief indications of the contents of six other works of Apollonius. These are *On Proportional Section* (181 propositions), *On Spatial Section* (124 propositions), *On Determinate Section* (83 propositions), *Tangencies* (124 propositions), *Vergings* (125 propositions), and *Plane Loci* (147 propositions). Only the first of these has survived, and this in Arabic. It deals with the general problem (see Fig. 1.5a): Given two lines *a* and *b* with the fixed points *A* on *a* and *B* on *b*, draw through a given point *O* a line *O A' B'* cutting *a* in *A'* and *b* in *B'* so that *AA'/BB' = k*, a given constant.

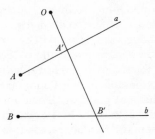

FIG. 1.5a

The exhaustiveness of the treatment is indicated by the fact that Apollonius considers 77 separate cases. The second work dealt with a similar problem, except that here we wish to have $(AA')(BB')$ $= k$. The third work concerned itself with the problem: Given four points *A, B, C, D* on a line, to find a point *P* on the line such that we have $(AP)(CP)/(BP)(DP) = k$. The work *Tangencies* dealt with the problem of constructing a circle tangent to three given circles, where the given circles are permitted to degenerate into straight lines or points. This problem, now known as the *problem of Apollonius,* has attracted many mathematicians and in the nineteenth century served as a sort of test problem in the competition between synthetic and analytic geometry. The general problem in *Vergings* was that of inserting a line segment between two given loci such that the line of the segment shall pass through a given point. In the last work, *Plane Loci,* appeared, among many others, the two theorems: (1) *If A and B are fixed points and k u given constant, then the locus of a point* P, *such that* AP/BP $= k$, *is either a circle (if k $\neq$ 1) or a straight line (if* k $= 1$*),* and (2) *If A, B, $\cdots$ are fixed points and.* a, b, $\cdots$, k *are given constants, then the locus of a point* P, *such that* a(AP)^2 + b(BP)^2+ $\cdots$ $= k$. *is a circle.* The circle of (1) is known, in modern college geometry texts, as a *circle of Apollonius.* Many attempts have been made to restore, from what little information we know of them, the above lost works of Apollonius.

With the passing of Apollonius the golden age of Greek geometry came to an end, and the lesser geometers who followed did little more than fill in details and perhaps independently develop certain theories the germs of which were already contained in the works of the three great predecessors. In particular, a number of new higher plane curves were discovered and the applications of geometry were exploited. Among these later geometers special mention should be made of Heron, Menelaus, Claudius Ptolemy, and Pappus. In geometry Heron largely concerned himself with plane and solid mensuration, and Menelaus and Ptolemy contributed to trigonometry as a handmaiden of astronomy. Pappus, the last of the creative Greek geometers, lived toward the end of the third century A.D., 500 years after Apollonius, and vainly strove with enthusiasm to rekindle fresh life into languishing Greek geometry. His great work, the *Collection*, most of which has come down to us, is a combined commentary and guidebook of the existing geometrical works of his time, sown with numerous original propositions, improvements, extensions, and valuable historical comments. There are many rich geometrical nuggets in the *Collection*, but it proved to be the requiem of Greek geometry, for after Pappus, Greek mathematics ceased to be a living study and we find merely its memory perpetuated by minor writers and commentators. Among these were Theon, Proclus, and Eutocius, the first known to us for his edition of Euclid's *Elements*, the second for the *Eudemian Summary* and his *Commentary on Euclid, Book I*, and the third for commentary on Archimedes.

In ancient Greek geometry, both in its form and in its content, we find the fountainhead of the subject. One can scarcely over-emphasize the importance to all subsequent geometry of this remarkable bequest of the ancient Greeks.

PROBLEMS

1.5-1   Let A, B, C denote 'the angles of a triangle; a, b, c the opposite sides; h_a, h_b, h_c the altitudes on these sides; m_a, m_b, m_c the medians to these sides; t_a, t_b, t_c the angle bisectors drawn to these sides; R and r the circumradius and inradius; b_a and c_a the projections of b and c on side a; and r_a the radius of the circle touching side a and sides b and c produced. Show that each of the following constitutes a datum:

(a) A, B, C

(b) $a/b, b/c, c/a$

(c) b, A, h_c

(d) $b + c, A, h_b + h_c$

(e) $b - c, A, h_c - h_b$

(f) $h_a, t_a, B - C$

(g) $h_a, m_a, b_a - c_a$

(h) $R, B - C, b_a - c_a$

(i) $R, r_a - r, a$

(j) h_a, r, r_a

1.5-2 Construct a triangle given (for notation see Problem 1.5-1):

(a) $a, A, h_b + h_c$

(b) $a - b, h_b + h_c, A$

(c) R, r, h_a

1.5-3 (a)   Complete the details of the following solution (essentially found in Euclid's work *On Divisions*) of the problem of constructing a straight line *GH* passing through a given point *D* within triangle *ABC*, cutting sides *BA* and *BC* in *G* and *H*, respectively, and such that triangles *GBH* and *ABC* have the same area (see Fig. 1.5b):

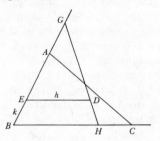

FIG. 1.5b

Draw *DE* parallel to *CB* to cut *AB* in *E*. Denote the lengths of *DE* and *EB* by *h* and *k*, respectively, and that of *GB* by *x*. Then $x(BH) = ac$. But $BH/h = x/(x - k)$. Eliminating *BH* we obtain $x^2 - mx + mk = 0$, where $m = ac/h$. Etc., by Problem 1.4-8 (b).

(b)   Solve the following problem, which is Proposition 28 in Euclid's work *On Divisions:* In Fig. 1.5c bisect the area *ABEC* by a straight line drawn through the midpoint *E* of the circular arc *BC*.

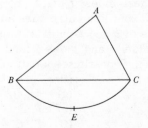

FIG. 1.5c

1.5-4 Let p_k and a_k denote the perimeter and the area of a regular k-gon inscribed in a given circle C, and let P_k and A_k denote the perimeter and the area of a regular k-gon circumscribed about the circle C. Show that

(a) $P_{2n} = 2p_n P_n / (p_n + P_n)$
(b) $p_{2n} = (p_n P_{2n})^{\frac{1}{2}}$
(c) $a_{2n} = (a_n A_n)^{\frac{1}{2}}$
(d) $A_{2n} = 2a_{2n} A_n / (a_{2n} + A_n)$

1.5-5 Cicero has related that when serving as Roman quaestor in Sicily he found and repaired Archimedes' then-neglected (but now vanished) tomb, upon which was engraved a sphere inscribed in a cylinder. This device commemorates Archimedes' favorite work, *On the Sphere and Cylinder*. Verify the following two results established by Archimedes in this work:

(a) The volume of the sphere is two-thirds that of the circumscribed cylinder.
(b) The area of the sphere is two-thirds of the total area of the circumscribed cylinder.
(c) Define *spherical zone* (of one and two bases), *spherical segment* (of one and two bases), and *spherical sector*.
(d) Assuming the theorem: *The area of a spherical zone is equal to the product of the circumference of a great circle and the altitude of the zone*, obtain the familiar formula for the area of a sphere and establish the theorem: *The area of a spherical zone of one base is equal to that of a circle whose radius is the chord of the generating arc*.

Assuming that the volume of a spherical sector is given by one-third the product of the area of its base and the radius of the sphere, obtain the following results:

(e) The volume of a spherical segment of one base, cut from a sphere of radius R, having h as altitude and a as the radius of its base, is given by

$$V = \pi h^2 (R - h/3) = \pi h (3a^2 + h^2) / 6.$$

(f) The volume of a spherical segment of two bases, having h as altitude and a and b as the radii of its bases, is given by

$$V = \pi h (3a^2 + 3b^2 + h^2)/6.$$

(g) The spherical segment of part (f) is equivalent to the sum of a sphere of radius $h/2$ and two cylinders whose altitudes are each $h/2$ and whose radii are a and b, respectively.

1.5-6 In his lost treatise on *Tangencies*, Apollonius considered the problem of drawing a circle tangent to three given circles A, B, C, where each of A, B, C may independently assume either of the degenerate forms of point or straight line. This problem has become known as the *problem of Apollonius.*

(a) Show that there are ten cases of the problem of Apollonius, depending on whether each of A, B, C is a point, a line, or a circle. What is the number of possible solutions for each case?

(b) Solve the problem where A, B, C are two points and a line.

(c) Reduce the problem where A, B, C are two lines and a point to the case of part (b).

1.5-7 (a) Solve the following easy verging problem considered by Apollonius in his work *Vergings:* In a given circle insert a chord of given length and verging to a given point.

A more difficult verging problem considered by Apollonius is: Given a rhombus with one side produced, insert a line segment of given length in the exterior angle so that it verges to the opposite vertex.

Let us be given two curves m and n, and a point O. Suppose that we permit ourselves to mark, on a given straightedge, a segment MN, and then to adjust the straightedge so that it passes through O and cuts the curves m and n with M on m and N on n. The line drawn along the straightedge is then said to have been drawn by "the insertion principle." Some problems beyond the Euclidean tools can be solved with these tools if we also permit ourselves to use the insertion principle. Establish the correctness of the following two such constructions.

(b) Let AB be a given segment. Draw angle $ABM = 90°$ and the angle $ABN = 120°$. Now draw ACD cutting BM in C and BN in D and such that $CD = AB$. Then $(AC)^3 = 2(AB)^3$, and we have a solution, using the insertion principle, of the ancient problem of duplicating a cube. Essentially the above construction was given by Viète and by Newton.

(c) Let AOB be any central angle in a given circle. Through B draw a line BCD cutting the circle again in C, AO produced in D, and such that $CD = OA$, the radius of the circle. Then angle $ADB = 1/3$ angle AOB. This solution of the famous problem of trisecting an angle is implied by a theorem given by Archimedes (*ca.* 240 B.C.).

1.5-8 Eratosthenes (*ca.* 230 B.C.) made a famous measurement

of the earth. He observed at Syene, at noon and at the summer
solstice, that a vertical stick had no shadow, while at Alexandria
(on the same meridian with Syene) the sun's rays were inclined
1/50 of a complete circle to the vertical. He then calculated
the circumference of the earth from the known distance of
5000 stades between Alexandria and Syene. Obtain Eratosthenes'
result of 250,000 stades for the circumference of the earth.
There is reason to suppose that a stade is about equal to
516.7 feet. Assuming this, calculate from the above result the
polar diameter of the earth in miles. (The actual polar diameter
of the earth, to the nearest mile, is 7900 miles.)

1.5-9 (a)   A regular heptagon (seven-sided polygon) cannot be
constructed with Euclidean tools. In his work *Metrica*, Heron
takes, for an approximate construction, the side of the heptagon
equal to the apothem (that is, the radius of the inscribed
circle) of a regular hexagon having the same circumcircle.
How good an approximation is this?

(b)   In *Catoptrica*, Heron proves, on the assumption that light
travels by the shortest path, that the angles of incidence and
reflection in a mirror are equal. Prove this.

(c)   A man wishes to go from his house to the bank of a straight
river for a pail of water, which he will then carry to his barn,
on the same side of the river as his house. Find the point on
the riverbank which will minimize the distance that the man
must travel.

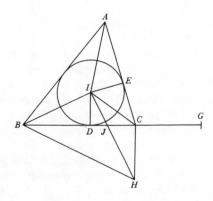

FIG. 1.5d

1.5-10 (a) Complete the details of the following indication of Heron's derivation of the formula for the area Δ of a triangle ABC in terms of its sides a, b, c. (1) Let the incircle, with center I and radius r, touch the sides BC, CA, AB in D, E, F, as in Fig. 1.5d. On BC produced take G such that $CG = AE$. Draw IH perpendicular to BI to cut BC in J and to meet the perpendicular to BC at C in H. (2) If $s = (a + b + c)/2$, then $\Delta = rs = (BG)(ID)$. (3) B, I, C, H lie on a circle, whence $\angle CHB$ is the supplement of $\angle BIC$ and hence is equal to $\angle EIA$. (4) $BC/CG = BC/AE = CH/IE = CJ/JD$. (5) $BG/CG = CD/JD$. (6) $(BG)^2/(CG)(BG) = (CD)(BD)/(JD)(BD) = (CD)(BD)/(ID)^2$. (7) $\Delta = (BG)(ID) = [(BG)(CG)(BD)(CD)]^{1/2} = [s(s - a)(s - b)(s - c)]^{1/2}$.

(b) Derive the formula of part (a) by the following process: Let h be the altitude on side c and let m be the projection of side b on side c. (1) Show that $m = (b^2 + c^2 - a^2)/2c$. (2) Substitute this value for m in $h = (b^2 - m^2)^{1/2}$. (3) Substitute this value for h in $\Delta = (ch)/2$.

1.5-11 (a) In Book III of Pappus's *Collection* we find the following interesting geometrical representation of some means. Take B on segment AC, B not being the midpoint O of AC. Erect the perpendicular to AC at B to cut the semicircle on AC in D, and let F be the foot of the perpendicular from B on OD. Show that OD, BD, FD represent the arithmetic mean, the geometric mean, and the harmonic mean, respectively, of the segments AB and BC, and show that, if $AB \neq BC$,

arith. mean > geom. mean > harm. mean.

(b) In Book III of the *Collection*, Pappus gives the following neat construction for the harmonic mean of the two given segments OA and OB in Fig. 1.5e. On the perpendicular to OB at B mark off $BD = BE$, and let the perpendicular to OB at A cut OD in F. Draw FE to cut OB in C. Then OC is the sought harmonic mean. Prove this.

(c) Let x be the side of a square inscribed in a triangle such that one side of the square lies along the base a of the triangle. Show that x is half the harmonic mean between a and h, where h is the altitude on the base a.

(d) Let a and b represent the lengths of two vertical poles, and let wires from the tip of each pole to the base of the other intersect at a distance x above ground. Prove that x is half the harmonic mean between a and b.

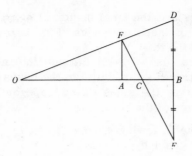

FIG. 1.5e

(e) Show that if a square is inscribed in a right triangle so
as to include the right angle of the triangle, then the side of the
square is equal to the product of the legs of the right triangle
divided by the sum of these legs.

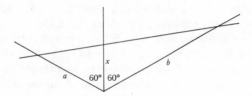

FIG. 1.5f

(f) In Fig. 1.5f, show that x is half the harmonic mean between
a and b. (This is the basis of a nomogram for the lens formula
of optics, wherein a, b, x represent the object distance, the

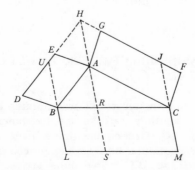

FIG. 1.5g

image distance, and the focal length, respectively, for a lens. Given any two of these distances, Fig. 1.5g gives us a ready construction of the third.)

(g) Show that the line segment through the intersection of the diagonals of a trapezoid, parallel to the bases of the trapezoid, and intercepted by the sides of the trapezoid is the harmonic mean of the bases of the trapezoid.

1.5-12 Prove the following elegant extension of the Pythagorean Theorem given by Pappus in Book IV of his *Collection* . Let ABC (see Fig. 1.5g) *be any triangle and* ABDE, ACFG *any parallelograms described externally on* AB *and* AC. *Let* DE *and* FG *meet in* H *and draw* BL *and* CM *equal and parallel to* HA. *Then*

$$\square \, BCML \;=\; \square ABDE \;+\; \square ACFG.$$

1.5-13 In Book VII of the *Collection*, Pappus anticipated one of the centroid theorems sometimes credited to P. Guldin (1577–1642). These theorems may be stated as follows: (1) *If a plane arc be revolved about an axis in its plane, but not cutting the arc, the area of the surface of revolution so formed is equal to the product of the length of the arc and the length of the path traced by the centroid of the arc.* (2) *If a plane area be revolved about an axis in its plane, but not intersecting the area, the volume of revolution so formed is equal to the product of the area and the length of the path traced by the centroid of the area.* Using these theorems, find

(a) The volume and surface area of the torus formed by revolving a circle of radius r about an axis, in the plane of this circle, at distance $R > r$ from the center of the circle.

(b) The centroid of a semicircular arc.

(c) The centroid of a semicircular area.

1.6   THE TRANSMISSION OF GREEK GEOMETRY TO THE OCCIDENT

The closing period of ancient times was dominated by Rome. One Greek center after another fell before the power of the Roman armies, and in 146 B.C. Greece became a province of the Roman Empire, though Mesopotamia was not conquered until 65 B.C. and Egypt held out until 30 B.C. Conditions proved more and more stifling to original scientific work, and a gradual decline in creative thinking set in. The arrival of the barbarians in the west and the eventual collapse of the slave market, with their disastrous effects on Roman economy, found science reduced to a mediocre level. The famous Alexandrian school gradually faded with the breakup of ancient society, becoming completely extinct in 641 A.D., when Alexandria was taken by the Arabs.

The period starting with the fall of the Roman Empire in the middle of the fifth century and extending into the eleventh century is known as Europe's Dark Ages, for during this period civilization in western Europe reached a very low ebb. Schooling became almost nonexistent, Greek learning all but disappeared, and many of the arts and crafts bequeathed by the ancient world were forgotten. Only the monks of the Catholic monasteries and a few cultured laymen preserved a slender thread of Greek and Latin learning. The period was marked by great physical violence and intense religious faith. The old social order gave way, and society became feudal and ecclesiastical.

The Romans had never taken to abstract mathematics but had contented themselves with merely a few practical aspects of the subject that were associated with commerce and civil engineering. With the fall of the Roman Empire and the subsequent closing of much of east-west trade and the abandonment of state engineering projects, even these interests waned, and it is no exaggeration to say that very little in mathematics, beyond the development of the Christian calendar, was accomplished in the West during the whole of the half millennium covered by the Dark Ages.

During this bleak period of learning, the people of the East, especially the Hindus and the Arabs, became the major custodians of mathematics. However, the Greek concept of rigorous thinking— in fact, the very idea of deductive proof—seemed distasteful to the Hindu way of doing things. Although the Hindus excelled in computation, contributed to the devices of algebra, and played an important role in the development of our present positional numeral system, they produced almost nothing of importance in geometry or in basic mathematical methodology.

The spectactular episode of the rise and decline of the Arabian Empire occurred during the period of Europe's Dark Ages. Within a decade following Mohammed's flight from Mecca to Medina in 622 A.D., the scattered and disunited tribes of the Arabian peninsula were consolidated by a strong religious fervor into a powerful nation. Within a century, force of arms had extended the Moslem rule and influence over a territory reaching from India, through Persia, Mesopotamia, and northern Africa, even into Spain. Of considerable importance for the preservation of much of world culture was the manner in which the Arabs seized upon Greek and Hindu erudition. The Baghdad caliphs not only governed wisely and well but many became patrons of learning and invited distinguished scholars to their courts. Numerous Hindu and Greek works in astronomy, medicine, and mathematics were industriously translated into the Arabic tongue and thus were saved until later European scholars were able to retranslate them into Latin and other languages. But for the work of the Arabian scholars a great part of Greek and Hindu science would have been irretrievably lost over the long period of the Dark Ages.

Not until the latter part of the eleventh century did Greek classics in science and mathematics begin once again to filter into Europe. There followed a period of transmission during which the ancient learning preserved by Moslem culture was passed on to the western Europeans through Latin translations made by Christian scholars traveling to Moslem centers of learning, and through the opening of western European commercial relations with the Levant and the Arabian world. The loss of Toledo by the Moors to the Christians in 1085 was followed by an influx of Christian scholars to that city to acquire Moslem learning. Other Moorish centers in Spain were infiltrated, and the twelfth century became, in the history of mathematics, a century of translators. One of the most industrious translators of the period was Gherardo of Cremona, who translated into Latin more than 90 Arabian works, among which were Ptolemy's *Almagest* and Euclid's *Elements*. At the same time Italian merchants came in close contact with Eastern civilization, thereby picking up useful arithmetical and algebraical information. These merchants played an important part in the European dissemination of the Hindu-Arabic numeral system.

The thirteenth century saw the rise of the universities at Paris, Oxford, Cambridge, Padua, and Naples. Universities were to become potent factors in the development of mathematics, since many mathematicians associated themselves with one or more such institutions. During this century Campanus made a Latin translation of Euclid's *Elements* which later, in 1482, became the first printed version of Euclid's great work.

The fourteenth century was a mathematically barren one. It was the century of the Black Death, which swept away more than a third of the population of Europe, and during this century the Hundred Years War, with its political and economic upheavals in northern Europe, got well under way.

The fifteenth century witnessed the start of the European

Renaissance in art and learning. With the collapse of the Byzantine Empire, culminating in the fall of Constantinople to the Turks in 1453, refugees flowed into Italy, bringing with them treasures of Greek civilization. Many Greek classics, up to that time known only through the often inadequate Arabic translations, could now be studied from original sources. Also, about the middle of the century, occurred the invention of printing, which revolutionized the book trade and enabled knowledge to be disseminated at an unprecedented rate. Mathematical activity in this century was largely centered in the Italian cities and in the central European cities of Nuremberg, Vienna, and Prague, and it concentrated on arithmetic, algebra, and trigonometry, under the practical influence of trade, navigation, astronomy, and surveying.

In the sixteenth century the development of arithmetic and algebra continued, the most spectacular mathematical achievement of the century—and the first really deep mathematical accomplishment beyond the Greeks and Arabs—being the discovery, by Italian mathematicians, of the algebraic solution of cubic and quartic equations. A decided stimulus to the further development of geometry was the translation, in 1533, of Proclus' *Commentary on Euclid, Book I*. The first important translation into Latin of Books I-IV of Apollonius' *Conic Sections* was made by Commandino in 1566; Books V-VII did not appear in Latin translation until 1661. In 1572 Commandino made a very important Latin translation of Euclid's *Elements* from the Greek. This translation served as a basis for many subsequent translations, including a very influential work by Robert Simson, from which, in turn, so many English editions were derived. By this time a number of the works of Archimedes had also been translated into Latin. With so many of the great Greek works in geometry available, it was inevitable that sooner or later some aspects of the subject should once again claim the attention of researchers.

PROBLEMS

1.6-1 Hindu arithmetical problems often involved the Pythagorean relation. Solve the following three such problems, the first two of which are adapted from problems given by Brahmagupta (*ca.* 630), and the last from a problem given by Bhāskara (*ca.* 1150).

(a) Two ascetics lived at the top of a cliff of height h, whose base was distant d from a neighboring village. One descended the cliff and walked to the village. The other, being a wizard, flew up a height x and then flew in a straight line to the village. The distance traversed by each was the same. Find x. (In the original problem $h = 100$ and $d = 200$.)

(b)   A bamboo 18 cubits high was broken by the wind. Its top touched the ground 6 cubits from the root. Tell the length of the segments of the bamboo.

(c)   A snake's hole is at the foot of a pillar which is 15 cubits high, and a peacock is perched on its summit. Seeing a snake, at a distance of thrice the pillar's height, gliding toward his hole, he pounces obliquely upon him. Say quickly at how many cubits from the snake's hole do they meet, both proceeding an equal distance?

1.6-2   (a)   Brahmagupta gave the formula

$$K^2 = (s - a)(s - b)(s - c)(s - d)$$

for the area K of a cyclic quadrilateral of sides a, b, c, d and semiperimeter s. Show that Heron's formula for the area of a triangle is a special case for this formula.

(b)   Using Brahmagupta's formula of part (a) show that the area of a quadrilateral possessing both an inscribed and a circumscribed circle is equal to the square root of the product of its four sides.

(c)   Show that a quadrilateral has perpendicular diagonals if and only if the sum of the squares of one pair of opposite sides is equal to the sum of the squares of the other pair of opposite sides.

(d)   Brahmagupta showed that if $a^2 + b^2 = c^2$ and $A^2 + B^2 = C^2$, then any quadrilateral having aC, cB, bC, cA for consecutive sides has perpendicular diagonals. Prove this.

(e)   If (a, b, c), (A, B, C) are two Pythagorean triples (that is, a, b, c, A, B, C are positive integers such that $a^2 + b^2 = c^2$ and $A^2 + B^2 = C^2$), then the cyclic quadrilateral having consecutive sides aC, cB, bC, cA is called a *Brahmagupta trapezium*. Find the sides, diagonals, circumradius, and area of the Brahmagupta trapezium determined by the two Pythagorean triples (3, 4, 5) and (5, 12, 13).

1.6-3   Many students of high school geometry have seen Bhā-skara's dissection proof of the Pythagorean Theorem, in which the square on the hypotenuse is cut up, as indicated in Fig. 1.6a, into four triangles, each congruent to the given triangle, plus   a square with side equal to the difference of the legs of the given triangle. The pieces are easily rearranged to give the sum of the squares on the two legs. Bhāskara drew the figure and offered no further explanation than the word "Behold!" Supply a proof.

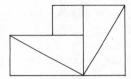

FIG. 1.6a

1.6-4   (a)   Given line segments of lengths a, b, n, construct, with Euclidean tools, a line segment of length $m = a^3/bn$.

(b)   Omar Khayyam ($ca.$ 1044-$ca.$ 1123) was the first to handle every type of cubic equation that possesses a positive root. Complete the details of the following sketch of Khayyam's geometrical solution of the cubic

$$x^3 + b^2x + a^3 = cx^2,$$

where a, b, c, x are thought of as lengths of line segments. Khayyam stated this type of cubic rhetorically as "a cube, some sides, and some numbers are equal to some squares."

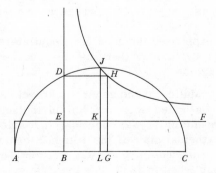

FIG. 1.6b

In Fig. 1.6b, construct $AB = a^3/b^2$ (by part (a)) and $BC = c$. Draw a semicircle on AC as diameter and let the perpendicular to AC at B cut it in D. On BD mark off $BE = b$, and through E draw EF parallel to AC. Find G on BC such that $(BG)(ED) = (BE)(AB)$ and complete the rectangle $DBGH$. Through H draw the rectangular hyperbola having EF and ED for asymptotes, and let it cut the semicircle in J. Let the parallel to DE through J cut EF in K and BC in L. Show, successively, that: (1) $(EK)(KJ) = (BG)(ED) = (BE)(AB)$, (2) $(BL)(LJ) = (BE)(AL)$, (3) $(LJ)^2 = (AL)(LC)$, (4) $(BE)^2/(BL)^2 = (LJ)^2/(AL)^2 = LC/AL$, (5) $(BE)^2(AL) = (BL)^2(LC)$, (6) $b^2(BL + a^3/b^2) = (BL)^2(c - BL)$, (7) $(BL)^3 + b^2(BL) + a^3 = c(BL)^2$. Thus BL is a root of the given cubic equation. (See J. L. Coolidge, *The Mathematics of Great Amateurs* (New York: Oxford University Press, 1949), chap. 2, "Omar Khayyam.")

1.6-5 The Arabians were interested in constructions on a spherical surface. Consider the following problems, to be solved with Euclidean tools and appropriate plane constructions.
(a) Given a material sphere, find its diameter.
(b) On a given material sphere locate the vertices of an inscribed cube.
(c) On a given material sphere locate the vertices of an inscribed regular tetrahedron.

1.6-6 The poverty of geometry in western Europe during the Dark Ages is illustrated by the following two problems considered by the famous French scholar and churchman, Gerbert (*ca.* 950-1003), who became Pope Sylvester II.
(a) In his *Geometry* Gerbert solved the problem, considered very difficult at the time, of determining the legs of a right triangle whose hypotenuse and area are given. Solve this problem.
(b) Gerbert expressed the area of an equilateral triangle of side a as $(a/2)(a - a/7)$. Show that this is not correct and is equivalent to taking $\sqrt{3} = 1.714$.

1.6-7 Johann Müller, more generally known as Regiomontanus, from the Latinized form of his birthplace of Königsberg ("king's mountain"), was perhaps the ablest and most influential mathematician of the fifteenth century. His treatise *De triangulis omnimodis,* which was written about 1464 but posthumously published in 1533, was the first systematic European exposition of plane and spherical trigonometry considered independently of astronomy. Solve the following three problems found in this work.

(a)   Determine a triangle given the difference of two sides, the altitude on the third side, and the difference of the segments into which the altitude divides the third side.

(b)   Determine a triangle given a side, the altitude on this side, and the ratio of the other two sides.

(c)   Construct a cyclic quadrilateral given the four sides.

1.6-8   Solve the following geometrical problem found in the *Sūma* of Luca Pacioli (*ca.* 1445-*ca.* 1509). The radius of the inscribed circle of a triangle is 4 and the segments into which one side is divided by the point of contact are 6 and 8. Determine the other two sides.

1.7   EMPIRICAL, OR EXPERIMENTAL, GEOMETRY

In Sec. 1.2 the empirical nature of pre-Hellenic geometry was considered, and it was pointed out that conclusions reached in this way may be incorrect and therefore cannot be regarded as established. To be assured that a conclusion incontestably follows from preliminary premises, deductive reasoning is necessary, and no amount of supporting empirical evidence will, of itself, suffice. For this reason the Greeks found in deductive reasoning the vital element of mathematical method, and they insisted that geometry—indeed, all mathematics—be developed via this process.

Since deductive reasoning has the advantage that its conclusions are unquestionable if the premises are accepted, whereas empirical procedure always leaves some room for doubt, one might over-hastily outlaw all empiricism and experimentation from geometry. This would be a grave mistake, for though today all *recorded* geometry is wholly deductive and completely bereft of any inductive element, it is probably quite true that few, if any, significant geometrical facts were ever found without some preliminary empirical work of one form or another. Before a geometrical statement can be proved or disproved by deduction, it must first be thought of, or conjectured, and a conjecture is nothing but a guess made more or less plausible by intuition, observation, analogy, experimentation, or some other form of empirical procedure. Deduction is a convincing formal mode of exposition, but it is hardly a means of discovery. It is a set of complicated machinery that needs material to work upon, and the material is usually furnished by empirical considerations. Even the steps of a deductive proof or disproof are not dictated to us by the deductive apparatus itself, but must be arrrived at by trial and error, experience, and shrewd guessing. Indeed, skill in the art of good guessing is one of the prime ingredients in the makeup of a worthy geometer.

To succeed in geometry, either as a creator or simply as a problem solver, one must be willing to experiment, to draw and test innumerable figures, to try this and to try that. Galileo (1564–1642), in 1599, attempted to ascertain the area under one arch of the cycloid curve‡ by balancing a cycloidal template against circular templates of the size of the generating circle. He incorrectly conjectured that the area under an arch is very nearly, but not exactly, three times the area of the circle. The first published mathematical demonstration that the area is exactly three times that of the generating circle was furnished, in 1644, by his pupil, Evangelista Torricelli (1608–1647), with the use of early integration methods.

Blaise Pascal (1623–1662), when a very young boy, "discovered" that the sum of the angles of a triangle is a straight angle by a simple experiment involving the folding of a paper triangle.

By actually constructing a right circular cone, three times filling it with sand and then emptying the contents into a right circular cylinder of the same radius and height, one would conjecture that the volume of a right circular cone is one-third the product of its altitude and the area of its circular base.

Suppose that one should take a horizontal circular disc and drive an upright nail into its center, and then coil a thick cord on the disc, in spiral fashion about the nail, until the disc is covered. This would require a piece of cord of a certain length. Now take a material hemisphere of the same radius as the disc and drive a nail into its pole. As before, coil a thick cord, now on the hemisphere, in spiral fashion about the nail, until the hemisphere is covered. It would be found that approximately twice as much cord is needed in the second experiment as was needed in the first one. From this it can be conjectured that the area of a sphere is four times the area of one of its great circles.

Many first-rate conjectures concerning maxima and minima problems in the calculus of variations were first obtained by soap-film experiments.

Archimedes, in his treatise on *Method*, has described how he first came to realize, by mechanical considerations, that the volume

‡A cycloid is the curve traced by a fixed point on the circumference of a circle which rolls, without slipping, along a straight line.

of a sphere is given by $4\pi r^3/3$, where r is the radius of the sphere. Here, briefly, is his process. Place the sphere with its polar diameter along a horizontal x axis with the north pole N at the origin (see Fig. 1.7a).

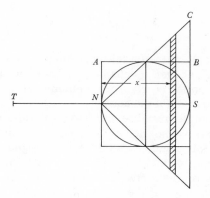

FIG. 1.7a

Construct the cylinder and the cone of revolution obtained by rotating the rectangle $NABS$ and the triangle NCS about the x axis. Now cut from the three solids thin vertical slices (assuming that they are flat cylinders) at distance x from N and of thickness Δx. The volumes of these slices are, approximately,

$$\text{sphere: } \pi x(2r - x)\Delta x,$$
$$\text{cylinder: } \pi r^2\Delta x,$$
$$\text{cone: } \pi x^2\Delta x.$$

Let us hang at T the slices from the sphere and the cone, where $TN = 2r$. Their combined moment§ about N is

$$[\pi x(2r - x)\Delta x + \pi x^2\Delta x]2r = 4\pi r^2 x\Delta x.$$

This, we observe, is four times the moment of the slice cut from the cylinder when that slice is left where it is. Adding a large number of these slices together we find

$$2r [\text{ vol. of sphere} + \text{vol. of cone}] = 4r [\text{ vol. of cylinder }],$$

_____

§By the *moment* of a volume about a point is here meant the product of the volume and the perpendicular distance from the point to the vertical line passing through the centroid of the volume.

or

$$2r \, [\text{ vol. of sphere } + \, 8\pi r^3 /3 \,] \, = \, 8\pi r^4 ,$$

or

$$\text{vol. of sphere } = \, 4\pi r^3 /3.$$

But Archimedes' mathematical conscience would not permit him to accept the above mechanical argument as a proof, and he accordingly supplied a rigorous demonstration employing the so-called Greek method of exhaustion.

One should not deprecate experiments and approaches of the above kind, for there is no doubt that much geometry has been "discovered" by such means. Of course, once a geometrical conjecture has been formulated, we must, like Archimedes, establish or disestablish it by deductive reasoning, and thus completely settle the matter one way or the other. Many a geometrical conjecture has been discarded by the outcome of just one carefully drawn figure, or by the examination of some extreme case.

A very fruitful way of making geometrical conjectures is by the employment of analogy, though it must be confessed that many conjectures so made are ultimately proved to be incorrect. An astonishing amount of space geometry has been discovered via analogy from similar situations in the plane, and in the geometry of higher dimensional spaces analogy has played a very successful role.

There is much to be said, at the elementary level of instruction, for empirical, or experimental, geometry, and many teachers feel it wise to precede a first course in demonstrative geometry with a few weeks of experimental geometry. The work of these weeks acquaints the student with many geometrical concepts, and can be designed to emphasize both the values and the shortcomings of empirical geometry. In fact, the geometry taught in the elementary grades might well be almost entirely of the scientific or experimental sort. Such instructional procedure follows the thesis that, in general, the learning program should parallel the historical development.

PROBLEMS

1.7-1 Does the process called "mathematical induction" have any induction in it? If so, where?

1.7-2   Show empirically, by a simple experiment involving the folding of a paper triangle, that the sum of the angles of a triangle is a straight angle.

1.7-3   If we cut off the top of a triangle by a line parallel to the base of the triangle, a trapezoid will remain, and the area of a trapezoid is given by the product of its altitude and the arithmetic average of its two bases. Now, if we cut off the top of a pyramid by a plane parallel to the base of the pyramid, a frustum will remain. Reasoning by analogy, obtain the incorrect Babylonian formula (see Sec. 1.2) for the volume of a frustum of a pyramid. (This illustrates that conclusions reached by analogy cannot be regarded as established.)

1.7-4   To trisect a central angle AOB of a circle, someone suggests that we trisect the chord AB and then join these points of trisection with O. While this construction may look somewhat reasonable for small angles, show, by taking an angle almost equal to $180°$, that the construction is patently false.

1.7-5   The three altitudes of a triangle are concurrent. Are the four altitudes of a tetrahedron concurrent?

1.7-6   A line segment has 2 zero-dimensional bounding elements (2 end points), and its interior is one-dimensional.

A triangle has 3 zero-dimensional and 3 one-dimensional bounding elements (3 vertices and 3 sides), and its interior is two-dimensional.

A tetrahedron has 4 zero-dimensional, 6 one-dimensional, and 4 two-dimensional bounding elements (4 vertices, 6 edges, 4 faces), and its interior is three-dimensional.

From this information, how many zero-, one-, two-, and three-dimensional bounding elements might you expect a pentatope (the four-dimensional analog of a tetrahedron) to have?

1.7-7   List the three-space analogs of the planar concepts *parallelogram, rectangle, circle* if (a) a tetrahedron, (b) a pyramid, is considered as the three-space analog of a triangle.

1.7-8   State theorems in three-space that are analogs of the following theorems in the plane.
(a)   The bisectors of the angles of a triangle are concurrent at the center of the inscribed circle of the triangle.
(b)   The area of a circle is equal to the area of a triangle the

base of which has the same length as the circumference of the circle and the altitude of which is equal to the radius of the circle.

(c) The foot of the altitude of an isosceles triangle is the mid-point of the base.

1.7-9 Two lines through the vertex of an angle and symmetrical with respect to the bisector of the angle are called a pair of *isogonal conjugate lines* of the angle. There is an attractive theorem about triangles which states that if three lines through the vertices of a triangle are concurrent, then the three isogonal conjugate lines through the vertices of the triangle are also concurrent. Try to construct an analogous definition and theorem for the tetrahedron.

1.7-10 Let F, V, E denote the number of faces, vertices, and edges of a polyhedron. For the tetrahedron, cube, triangular prism, pentagonal prism, square pyramid, pentagonal pyramid, cube with one corner cut off, cube with a square pyramid erected on one face, we find that $V - E + F = 2$. Do you feel that this formula holds for *all* polyhedra? Consider the one pictured in Fig. 1.7b.

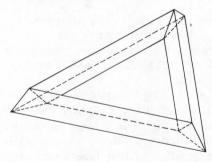

FIG. 1.7b

1.7-11 There are convex polyhedra all faces of which are triangles (for instance a tetrahedron), all faces of which are quadrilaterals (for instance a cube), all faces of which are pentagons (for instance a regular dodecahedron). Do you think that the list can be continued?

1.7-12 (a) Consider a convex polyhedron P and let C be any point in its interior. We can imagine a suitable heterogeneous distribution of mass within P such that the center of gravity of P will coincide with C. If the polyhedron is thrown upon a horizontal floor, it will come to rest on one of its faces. Show that this yields a mechanical argument for the geometrical proposition: "Given a convex polyhedron P and a point C in its interior, then there exists a face F of P such that the foot of the perpendicular from C to the plane of F lies in the interior of F."

(b)   Give a geometrical proof of the proposition of part (a).

II. MODERN ELEMENTARY GEOMETRY

The period following the European Renaissance, and running into present times, is known in the history of mathematics as the *modern era*. One of the ways in which mathematicians of the modern era have extended geometry beyond that inherited from the Greeks has been by the discovery of a host of further propositions about circles and rectilinear figures deduced from those listed in Euclid's *Elements*. This material is referred to as *modern elementary geometry*, and it constitutes a sequel to, or expansion of, Euclid's *Elements*. The nineteenth century witnessed an astonishing growth in this area of geometry, and the number of papers in the subject which have since appeared is almost unbelievable. In 1906, Maximilian Simon (in his *Über die Entwickelung der Elementargeometrie im XIX. Jahrhundert*) attempted the construction of a catalog of contributions to elementary geometry made during the nineteenth century; it has been estimated that this catalog contains upward of 10,000 references! Research in the field has not abated, and it would seem that the geometry of the triangle and its associated points, lines, and circles must be inexhaustible. Much of the material has been extended to the tetrahedron and its associated points, lines, planes, and spheres, resulting in an enormous and beautiful expansion of elementary solid geometry.

Here is a singularly fascinating, highly intricate, extensive, and challenging field of mathematics that can be studied and pursued with very little mathematical prerequisite and with a fair chance of making an original discovery. The subject, though elementary, is often far from easy. Large portions of the material have been summarized and organized into textbooks bearing the title of modern, or college, geometry. On the grounds that "you cannot lead anyone farther than you have gone yourself," a course following one of these texts is highly desirable for anyone preparing to teach geometry in high school. In this chapter we shall briefly consider a few selected topics from modern elementary geometry. Much of this material has, in one way or another, entered into the mainstream of mathematics.

2.1   SENSED MAGNITUDES

One of the innovations of modern elementary geometry is the employment, when it proves useful, of sensed, or signed, magnitudes. It was the extension of the number system so as to include both positive and negative numbers that led to this forward step in geometry, and though Albert Girard, René Descartes, and others introduced negative segments into geometry during the seventeenth century, the idea of sensed magnitudes was first systematically exploited in the early nineteenth century by L.N.M. Carnot (in his *Géométrie de position* of 1803) and especially by A.F. Möbius (in his *Der barycentrische Calcul* of 1827). By means of the concept of sensed magnitudes, several separate statements or relations can often be combined into a single embracive statement or relation, and a single proof can frequently be formulated for a theorem that would otherwise require the treatment of a number of different cases.

We start a study of sensed magnitudes with some definitions and a notation.

2.1.1   *Definitions and Notation.* Sometimes we shall choose one direction along a given straight line as the positive direction, and the other direction as the negative direction. A segment AB on the line will then be considered *positive* or *negative* according as the direction from A to B is the positive or negative direction of the line, and the symbol $\overline{AB}$ (in contrast to AB) will be used to denote the resulting signed distance from the point A to the point B. Such a segment $\overline{AB}$ is called a *sensed,* or *directed, segment*; point A is called   the *initial point* of the segment and point B is called the *terminal point* of the segment. The fact that $\overline{AB}$ and $\overline{BA}$ are equal in magnitude but opposite in direction is indicated by the equation

$$\overline{AB} = -\ \overline{BA},$$

or by the equivalent equation

$$\overline{AB} + \overline{BA} = 0.$$

Of course $\overline{AA} = 0$.

    2.1.2 *Definitions.*   Points which lie on the same straight line are said to be *collinear*. A set of collinear points is said to constitute a *range* of points, and the straight line on which they lie is called the *base* of the range.

We are now in a position to establish a few basic theorems about sensed line segments.

    2.1.3 *Theorem.*   *If* A, B, C *are any three collinear points, then*

$$\overline{AB} + \overline{BC} + \overline{CA} = 0.$$

If the points A, B, C are distinct, then C must lie between A and B, or on the prolongation of $\overline{AB}$, or on the prolongation of $\overline{BA}$. We consider these three cases in turn.

If C lies between A and B, then $\overline{AB} = \overline{AC} + \overline{CB}$, or $\overline{AB} - \overline{CB}$ $\overline{AC} = 0$, or $\overline{AB} + \overline{BC} + \overline{CA} = 0$.

If C lies on the prolongation of $\overline{AB}$, then $\overline{AB} + \overline{BC} = \overline{AC}$, or $\overline{AB} + \overline{BC} - \overline{AC} = 0$, or $\overline{AB} + \overline{BC} + \overline{CA} = 0$.

If C lies on the prolongation of $\overline{BA}$, then $\overline{CA} + \overline{AB} = \overline{CB}$, or $\overline{AB} - \overline{CB} + \overline{CA} = 0$, or $\overline{AB} + \overline{BC} + \overline{CA} = 0$.

The situations where one or more of the points A, B, C coincide are easily disposed of.

This theorem illustrates one of the economy features of sensed magnitudes. Without the concept of directed line segments, three separate equations would have to be given to describe the possible relations connecting the three unsigned distances AB, BC, CA between pairs of the three distinct collinear points A, B, C.

    2.1.4 *Theorem.*   *Let* O *be any point on the line segment* AB. *Then* $\overline{AB}$ $= \overline{OB} - \overline{OA}$.

This is an immediate consequence of Theorem **2.1.3**, for by that theorem we have $\overline{AB} + \overline{BO} + \overline{OA} = 0$, whence $\overline{AB} = -\overline{BO} - \overline{OA}$ $= \overline{OB} - \overline{OA}$.

    2.1.5 *Euler's Theorem* (1747).   *If* A, B, C, D *are any four collinear points, then*

$$\overline{AD} \cdot \overline{BC} + \overline{BD} \cdot \overline{CA} + \overline{CD} \cdot \overline{AB} = 0.$$

The theorem follows by noting that, by Theorem 2.1.4, the left member of the above equation may be put in the form

$$\overline{AD}(\overline{DC} - \overline{DB}) + \overline{BD} (\overline{DA} - \overline{DC}) + \overline{CD} (\overline{DB} - \overline{DA}),$$

which, upon expansion and reduction, is found to vanish identically.

The notion of directed segment leads to the following very useful definition of the ratio in which a point on a line divides a segment on that line.

2.1.6 *Definitions.* If A, B, P are distinct collinear points, we define *the ratio in which* P *divides the segment* AB to be the ratio $\overline{AP} / \overline{PB}$. It is to be noticed that the value of this ratio is independent of any direction assigned to line AB. If P lies between A and B, the division is said to be *internal*; otherwise the division is said to be *external*. Denoting the ratio $\overline{AP} / \overline{PB}$ by r, we note that if P lies on the prolongation of $\overline{BA}$, then $-1 < r < 0$; if P lies between A and B, then $0 < r < \infty$; if P lies on the prolongation of $\overline{AB}$, then $-\infty < r < -1$.

If A and B are distinct and P coincides with A, we set $\overline{AP} / \overline{PB} = 0$. If A and B are distinct and P coincides with B, the ratio $\overline{AP} / \overline{PB}$ is undefined and we indicate this by writing $\overline{AP} / \overline{PB} = \infty$.

Workers in modern elementary geometry have devised several ways of assigning a sense to angles lying in a common plane, and each way has its own uses. The way we are about to describe is particularly useful in relations involving trigonometric functions.

2.1.7 *Definitions and Notation.* We may consider $\angle AOB$ as generated by the rotation of side OA about point O until it coincides with side OB, the rotation not exceeding $180°$. If the rotation is counterclockwise the angle is said to be *positive*; if the rotation is clockwise the angle is said to be *negative*, and the symbol $\angle \overline{AOB}$ (in contrast to $\angle AOB$) will be used to denote the resulting signed rotation. Such an $\angle \overline{AOB}$ is called a *sensed*, or *directed*, *angle*; point O is called the *vertex* of the angle; side OA is called the *initial side* of the angle; side OB is called the *terminal side* of the angle. If $\angle AOB$ is not a straight angle, then the fact that $\angle \overline{AOB}$ and $\angle \overline{BOA}$ are equal in magnitude but opposite in direction is indicated by the equation

$$\angle \overline{AOB} = - \angle \overline{BOA},$$

or by the equivalent equation

$$\angle \overline{AOB} + \angle \overline{BOA} = 0.$$

It is sometimes convenient to assign a sense to the areas of triangles lying in a common plane.

2.1.8   *Definitions and Notation.*   A triangle ABC will be considered as *positive* or *negative* according as the tracing of the perimeter from A to B to C to A is counterclockwise or clockwise. Such a signed triangular area is called a *sensed*, or *directed, area*, and will be denoted by $\triangle\overline{ABC}$ (in contrast to $\triangle ABC$).

Some subsequent developments in this chapter will make use of the following two important theorems.

2.1.9   *Theorem.*   *If vertex A of triangle ABC is joined to any point L on line* BC, *then*

$$\frac{\overline{BL}}{\overline{LC}} = \frac{AB \sin \overline{BAL}}{AC \sin \overline{LAC}}.$$

Let h denote the length of the perpendicular from A to line BC. The reader may then check that for all possible figures,

$$\frac{\overline{BL}}{\overline{LC}} = \frac{h\overline{BL}}{h\overline{LC}} = \frac{2\triangle\overline{ABL}}{2\triangle\overline{ALC}} = \frac{(AB)(AL)\sin\overline{BAL}}{(AL)(AC)\sin\overline{LAC}} = \frac{AB\sin\overline{BAL}}{AC\sin\overline{LAC}}.$$

2.1.10   *Theorem.*   *If* a, b, c, d *are four distinct lines passing through a point* V, *then*

$$(\sin \overline{AVC} \ / \ \sin \overline{CVB}) \ / \ (\sin \overline{AVD} \ / \ \sin \overline{DVB})$$

is independent of the positions of A, B, C, D *on the lines* a, b, c, d, *respectively, so long as they are all distinct from* V.

We leave it to the reader to supply a proof of this theorem.

We now close the present section with the following convenient definitions.

2.1.11   *Definitions*   Straight lines which lie in a plane and pass through a common point are said to be *concurrent*. A set of concurrent coplanar lines is said to constitute a *pencil* of lines, and the point through which they all pass is called the *vertex* of the pencil. A line in the plane of a pencil and not passing through the vertex of the pencil is called a *transversal* of the pencil.

PROBLEMS

2.1-1 If $A_1, A_2, \ldots, A_n$ are n collinear points, show that

$$\overline{A_1A_2} + \overline{A_2A_3} + \cdots + \overline{A_{n-1}A_n} + \overline{A_nA_1} = 0.$$

2.1-2 If A, B, P are collinear and M is the midpoint of AB, show that $\overline{PM} = (\overline{PA} + \overline{PB})/2$.

2.1-3 If O, A, B are collinear, show that $\overline{OA}^2 + \overline{OB}^2 = \overline{AB}^2 + 2(\overline{OA})(\overline{OB})$.

2.1-4 If O, A, B, C are collinear and $\overline{OA} + \overline{OB} + \overline{OC} = 0$ and if P is any point on the line AB, show that $\overline{PA} + \overline{PB} + \overline{PC} = 3\overline{PO}$.

2.1-5 If on the same line we have $\overline{OA} + \overline{OB} + \overline{OC} = 0$ and $\overline{O'A'} + \overline{O'B'} + \overline{O'C'} = 0$, show that $\overline{AA'} + \overline{BB'} + \overline{CC'} = 3\overline{OO'}$.

2.1-6 If A, B, C are collinear and if P, Q, R are midpoints of BC, CA, AB respectively, show that the midpoints of CR and PQ coincide.

2.1-7 Let a and b be two given (positive) segments. Construct points P and Q on AB such that $\overline{AP}/\overline{PB} = a/b$ and $\overline{AQ}/\overline{QB} = -a/b$.

2.1-8 Show that if two points divide a line segment AB in equal ratios, then the two points coincide.

2.1-9 If AL is the bisector of angle A in triangle ABC, show that $\overline{BL}/\overline{LC} = AB/AC$.

2.1-10 If AL is the bisector of exterior angle A of triangle ABC, where $AB \neq AC$, show that $\overline{BL}/\overline{LC} = -AB/AC$.

2.1-11 Prove Stewart's Theorem: If A, B, C are any three points on a line and P any point, then $(\overline{PA}^2 \cdot \overline{BC}) + (\overline{PB}^2 \cdot \overline{CA}) + (\overline{PC}^2 \cdot \overline{AB}) + (\overline{BC} \cdot \overline{CA} \cdot \overline{AB}) = 0$. (This theorem was stated, without proof, by Matthew Stewart (1717-1785) in 1746; it was rediscovered and proved by Thomas Simpson (1710-1761) in 1751, by L. Euler in 1780, and by L.N.M.Carnot in 1803. The case where P lies on the line ABC if found in Pappus' *Collection*.)

2.1-12 Find the lengths of the medians of a triangle having sides a, b, c.

2.1-13 Find the lengths of the angle bisectors of a triangle having sides a, b, c.

2.1-14 Give a direct proof of the Steiner–Lehmus Theorem: If the bisectors of the base angles of a triangle are equal, the triangle is isosceles. (This problem was proposed in 1840 by D.C. Lehmus (1780–1863) to Jacob Steiner (1796–1863).)

2.1-15 Show that the sum of the squares of the distances of the vertex of a right angle of a right triangle from the two points of trisection of the hypotenuse is equal to 5/9 the square of the hypotenuse.

2.1-16 If A, B, C, D, O are any five coplanar points, show that
(a) $\sin \overline{AOD} \sin \overline{BOC} + \sin \overline{BOD} \sin \overline{COA} + \sin \overline{COD} \sin \overline{AOB} = 0$.
(b) $\triangle \overline{AOD}\triangle \overline{BOC} + \triangle \overline{BOD}\triangle \overline{COA} + \triangle \overline{COD}\triangle \overline{AOB} = 0$.

2.1-17 Using Problem 2.1-16(a) prove Ptolemy's Theorem: If $ABCD$ is a cyclic quadrilateral, then $AD \cdot BC + AB \cdot CD = AC \cdot BD$.

2.1-18 If O is any point in the plane of triangle ABC, show that

$$\triangle \overline{OBC} + \triangle \overline{OCA} + \triangle \overline{OAB} = \triangle \overline{ABC}.$$

2.1-19 If A, B, C, D, P, Q are any six distinct collinear points, show that

$$(\overline{AP} \cdot \overline{AQ})/(\overline{AB} \cdot \overline{AC} \cdot \overline{AD}) + (\overline{BP} \cdot \overline{BQ})/(\overline{BC} \cdot \overline{BD} \cdot \overline{BA})$$

$$+ (\overline{CP} \cdot \overline{CQ})/(\overline{CD} \cdot \overline{CA} \cdot \overline{CB})$$

$$+ (\overline{DP} \cdot \overline{DQ})/(\overline{DA} \cdot \overline{DB} \cdot \overline{DC}) = 0.$$

2.1-20 Prove Theorem 2.1.10.

2.2   INFINITE ELEMENTS

Another innovation of modern elementary geometry is the creation of some ideal elements called "points at infinity," "the line at infinity" in a plane, and "the plane at infinity" in space. The purpose of introducing these ideal elements is to eliminate certain bothersome case distinctions in plane and solid geometry which arise from the possibility of lines and planes being either parallel or intersecting. It follows that with these ideal elements many theorems can be given a single universal statement, whereas without these ideal elements the statements have to be qualified to take care of various exceptional situations. Subterfuges of this sort are common in mathematics. Consider, for example, the discussion of quadratic equations in elementary algebra. The equation $x^2 - 2x + 1 = 0$ actually has only the one root, $x = 1$, but for the sake of uniformity it is agreed to say that the equation has *two equal roots*, each equal to 1. Again, in order that the equation $x^2 + x + 1 = 0$ have any root at all, it is agreed to extend the number system so as to include imaginary numbers. With these two conventions — that a repeated root is to count as two roots and that imaginary roots are to be accepted equally with real roots — we can assert as a universal statement that "every quadratic equation with real coefficients has exactly two roots."

The introduction into geometry of the notion of points at infinity is usually credited to Johann Kepler (1571-1630), but it was Gérard Desargues (1593-1662) who, in a treatment of the conic sections (his *Brouillon projet*) published in 1639, first used the idea systematically. This work of Desargues marks the first essential advance in synthetic geometry since the time of the ancient Greeks.

Restricting ourselves for the time being to plane geometry, consider two lines l_1 and l_2, where l_1 is held fast while l_2 rotates about a fixed point O in the plane but not on line l_1. As l_2 approaches the position of parallelism with l_1, the point P of intersection of l_1 and l_2 recedes farther and farther along line l_1, and in the limiting position of parallelism the point P ceases to exist. To accommodate this exceptional situation, we agree to augment the set of points on l_1 by an ideal point, called *the point at infinity* on l_1, and we say that when l_1 and l_2 are parallel they intersect in this ideal point on l_1.

If our introduction of an ideal point at infinity on a line is not to create more exceptions than it removes, it must be done in such a way that two distinct points, ordinary or ideal, determine one and only one line, and such that two distinct lines intersect in one and only one point. As a first consequence of this we see that two parallel lines must intersect in the same ideal point, no matter in which direction the lines are traversed.

Suppose that l_1 and l_2 are two parallel lines intersecting in the ideal point I, and let O be any ordinary point not on l_1 or l_2. Since O and I are to determine a line l_3, and since l_3 cannot intersect l_1 or l_2 a second time, we see that l_3 must be the parallel to l_1 and l_2 through point O. That is, the ideal point I lies on all three of the parallel lines l_1, l_2, l_3, and, by the same argument, on all lines parallel to l_1. Thus the members of a family of parallel lines must share a common ideal point at infinity.

It is easy to see that a different ideal point must be assigned for a different family of parallel lines. For let line m_1 cut line l_1 in an ordinary point P, and let m_2 be a line parallel to m_1. Then m_1 and m_2 intersect in an ideal point J which must be distinct from I, since otherwise the distinct lines m_1 and l_1 would intersect in the two points P and I.

Now consider two distinct ideal points I and J. The line l which they are to determine cannot pass through any ordinary point P of the plane. For if it did, then line l_1 determined by P and I and line l_2 determined by P and J would be a pair of distinct ordinary lines each of which would be contained in line l because of the collinearity of P, I, J. It follows that the line l determined by a pair of ideal points can contain only ideal points and must therefore be an ideal line, which we call a *line at infinity*.

Finally, we see that in the plane there can be only one line at infinity. For if l_1 and l_2 should be two distinct lines at infinity, these lines would have to intersect in an ideal point I. A line l_3 passing through an ordinary point O and not passing through I would have to intersect l_1 and l_2 in distinct ideal points J and K, respectively. The line through J and K would then contain the ordinary point O, which we have seen is impossible.

The above discussion leads to the following convention and theorem.

2.2.1   *Convention and Definitions.*   We agree to add to the points of the plane a collection of ideal points, called *points at infinity,* such that

(1)   each ordinary line of the plane contains exactly one ideal point,

(2)   the members of a family of parallel lines in the plane share a common ideal point, distinct families having distinct ideal points.

The collection of added ideal points is regarded as an ideal line, called the *line at infinity,* which contains no ordinary points.

The plane, augmented by the above ideal points, will be referred to as the *extended plane.*

2.2.2   *Theorem.*   *In the extended plane, any two distinct points determine one and only one line and any two distinct lines intersect in one and only one point.*

If a point P recedes indefinitely along the line determined by two ordinary points A and B, then $\overline{AP}/\overline{PB}$ approaches the limiting value -1. This motivates the following definition.

2.2.3 *Definition.*   If A and B are any two ordinary points, and I the ideal point, on a given line, then we define $\overline{AI} \,/\, \overline{IB}$ to be -1.

A similar analysis can be supplied leading to the following convention, definitions, and theorem for three-dimensional space.

2.2.4 *Convention and Definitions.*   We agree to add to the points of space a collection of ideal points, called *points at infinity*, and ideal lines, called *lines at infinity*, such that

(1)   each ordinary line of space contains exactly one ideal point,

(2)   the members of a family of parallel lines in space share a common ideal point, distinct families having distinct ideal points,

(3)   each ordinary plane of space contains exactly one ideal line,

(4)   the members of a family of parallel planes in space share a common ideal line, distinct families having distinct ideal lines,

(5)   the ideal line of an ordinary plane in space consists of the ideal points of the ordinary lines of that plane.

The collection of added ideal points and ideal lines is regarded as an ideal plane, called the *plane at infinity*, which contains no ordinary points or lines.

Three-dimensional space augmented by the above ideal elements will be referred to as *extended three-dimensional space*.

2.2.5 *Theorem.   In extended three-dimensional space, any two distinct coplanar lines intersect in one and only one point, any nonincident line and plane intersect in one and only one point, any three noncoaxial planes* (that is, planes not sharing a common line) *intersect in one and only one point, any two distinct planes intersect in one and only one line, any two distinct points determine one and only one line, any two distinct intersecting lines determine one and only one plane, any nonincident point and line determine one and only one plane, any three noncollinear points determine one and only one plane.*

PROBLEMS

2.2-1   Which of the following statements are true for the ordinary plane and which are true for the extended plane?

(a)   There is a one-to-one correspondence between the lines through a fixed point O and the points of a fixed line l, not passing through O, such that corresponding lines and points are in incidence.

(b) The bisector of an exterior angle of an ordinary triangle divides the opposite side externally in the ratio of the adjacent sides.

(c) Every straight line possesses one and only one ideal point.

(d) Every straight line possesses infinitely many ordinary points.

(e) If a triangle is the figure determined by any three non-concurrent straight lines, then every triangle encloses a finite area.

(f) If parallel lines are lines lying in the same plane and having no ordinary point in common, then through a given point O there passes one and only one line parallel to a given line l not containing O.

(g) If A and B are distinct ordinary points and r is any real number, there is a unique point P on line AB such that $\overline{AP}/\overline{PB} = r$.

2.2-2 Translate the following theorems of ordinary three-dimensional space into the language of infinite elements, and then supply simple proofs.

(a) Through a given point there is one and only one plane parallel to a given plane not containing the given point.

(b) Two lines which are parallel to a third line are parallel to each other.

(c) If a line is parallel to each of two intersecting planes it is parallel to their line of intersection.

(d) If a line is parallel to the line of intersection of two intersecting planes, then it is parallel to each of the two planes.

(e) If a line l is parallel to a plane p, then any plane containing l and intersecting p cuts p in a line parallel to l.

(f) Through a given line one and only one plane can be passed parallel to a given skew line.

(g) Through a given point one and only one plane can be passed parallel to each of two skew lines, neither of which contains the given point.

(h) All the lines through a point and parallel to a given plane lie in a plane parallel to the first plane.

(i) If a plane contains one of two parallel lines but not the other, then it is parallel to the other.

(j) The intersections of a plane with two parallel planes are parallel lines.

2.2-3 Define prism and cylinder in terms of pyramid and cone respectively.

2.2-4 If A, B, C, P, Q are any five collinear points, show that

$$(\overline{AP} \cdot \overline{AQ})/(\overline{AB} \cdot \overline{AC}) + (\overline{BP} \cdot \overline{BQ})/(\overline{BC} \cdot \overline{BA})$$
$$+ (\overline{CP} \cdot \overline{CQ})/(\overline{CA} \cdot \overline{CB}) = 1.$$

2.2-5 If A, B, C, D, P are any five collinear points, show that

$$\overline{AP}/(\overline{AB} \cdot \overline{AC} \cdot \overline{AD}) + \overline{BP}/(\overline{BC} \cdot \overline{BD} \cdot \overline{BA}) + \overline{CP}/(\overline{CD} \cdot \overline{CA} \cdot \overline{CB})$$
$$+ \overline{DP}/(\overline{DA} \cdot \overline{DB} \cdot \overline{DC}) = 0.$$

2.3   THE THEOREMS OF MENELAUS AND CEVA

The theorems of Menelaus and Ceva, in their original versions, are quite old, for the one dates back to ancient Greece and the other to 1678. It is when they are stated in terms of sensed magnitudes that they assume a particularly modern appearance.

Menelaus of Alexandria was a Greek astronomer who lived in the first century A.D. Though his works in their original Greek are all lost to us, we know of some of them from remarks made by later commentators, and his three-book treatise *Sphaerica* has been preserved for us in the Arabic. In this work is developed the spherical trigonometry of the time, largely deduced from the spherical analog of the plane proposition now commonly referred to as *Menelaus' Theorem*. Actually, the plane case is assumed by Menelaus as well known and is used by him to establish the spherical case. A good deal of spherical trigonometry can be deduced from the spherical version of the theorem by taking special triangles and special transversals. L. N. M. Carnot made the theorem of Menelaus basic in his *Essai sur la théorie des transversales* of 1806.

Though the theorem of Ceva is a close companion theorem to that of Menelaus, it seems to have eluded discovery until 1678, when the Italian Giovanni Ceva (*ca.* 1647−1736) published a work containing both it and the then apparently long-forgotten theorem of Menelaus.

The theorems of Menelaus and Ceva, in their modern dress, are powerful theorems, and they deal elegantly with many problems involving collinearity of points and concurrency of lines. We now turn to a study of these two remarkable theorems. The reader should observe how the convention as to points at infinity eliminates the separate consideration of a number of otherwise exceptional situations.

2.3.1 *Definition.*   A point lying on a side line of a triangle, but not coinciding with a vertex of the triangle, will be called a *menelaus point* of the triangle for this side.

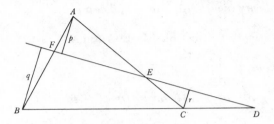

Fig. 2.3a

2.3.2 *Menelaus' Theorem.   A necessary and sufficient condition for three menelaus points* D, E, F *for the sides* BC, CA, AB *of an ordinary triangle* ABC *to be collinear is that*

$$(\overline{BD}/\overline{DC})(\overline{CE}/\overline{EA})(\overline{AF}/\overline{FB}) = -1.$$

Necessity: Suppose (see Fig. 2.3a) that *D, E, F* are collinear on a line *l* which is not the line at infinity. Drop perpendiculars *p, q, r* on *l* from *A, B, C*. Then, disregarding signs,

$$BD/DC = q/r, \; CE/EA = r/p, \; AF/FB = p/q.$$

It follows that

$$(\overline{BD}/\overline{DC})(\overline{CE}/\overline{EA})(\overline{AF}/\overline{FB}) = \pm 1.$$

Since, however, *l* must cut one or all three sides externally, we see that we can have only the − sign. If *l* is the line at infinity, the proof is simple.
Sufficiency: Suppose that

$$(\overline{BD}/\overline{DC})(\overline{CE}/\overline{EA})(\overline{AF}/\overline{FB}) = -1$$

and let *EF* cut *BC* in *D'*. Then *D'* is a menelaus point and, by the above,

$$(\overline{BD'}/\overline{D'C})(\overline{CE}/\overline{EA})(\overline{AF}/\overline{FB}) = -1.$$

It follows that $\overline{BD}/\overline{DC} = \overline{BD'}/\overline{D'C}$, or that $D \equiv D'$. That is, D, E, F are collinear.

2.3.3   *Trigonometric Form of Menelaus' Theorem.*   *A necessary and sufficient condition for three menelaus points* D, E, F *for the sides* BC, CA, AB *of an ordinary triangle* ABC *to be collinear is that*

$$(\sin \overline{BAD}/\sin \overline{DAC})(\sin \overline{CBE}/\sin \overline{EBA})(\sin \overline{ACF}/\sin \overline{FCB}) = -1.$$

For we have, by Theorem 2.1.9,

$$\overline{BD}/\overline{DC} = (AB \sin \overline{BAD})/(AC \sin \overline{DAC}),$$

$$\overline{CE}/\overline{EA} = (BC \sin \overline{CBE})/(BA \sin \overline{EBA}),$$

$$\overline{AF}/\overline{FB} = (CA \sin \overline{ACF})/(CB \sin \overline{FCB}).$$

It follows that

$$(\sin \overline{BAD}/\sin \overline{DAC})(\sin \overline{CBE}/\sin \overline{EBA})(\sin \overline{ACF}/\sin \overline{FCB}) = -1$$

if and only if

$$(\overline{BD}/\overline{DC})(\overline{CE}/\overline{EA})(\overline{AF}/\overline{FB}) = -1.$$

Hence the theorem.

2.3.4   *Definition.*   A line passing through a vertex of a triangle, but not coinciding with a side of the triangle, will be called a *cevian line* of the triangle for this vertex. A cevian line will be identified by the vertex to which it belongs and the point in which it cuts the opposite side, as cevian line AD through vertex A of triangle ABC and cutting the opposite side BC in the point D.

2.3.5   *Ceva's Theorem.*   *A necessary and sufficient condition for three cevian lines* AD, BE, CF *of an ordinary triangle* ABC *to be concurrent is that*

$$(\overline{BD}/\overline{DC})(\overline{CE}/\overline{EA})(\overline{AF}/\overline{FB}) = +1.$$

Necessity: Suppose (see Fig. 2.3b) that AD, BE, CF are concurrent in P. Without loss of generality we may assume that P does not lie on the parallel through A to BC. Let BE, CF intersect this parallel in N and M. Then, disregarding signs,

$$BD/DC = AN/MA, \quad CE/EA = BC/AN, \quad AF/FB = MA/BC,$$

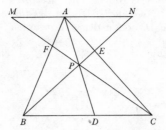

Fig. 2.3b

whence

$$(\overline{BD}/\overline{DC})(\overline{CE}/\overline{EA})(\overline{AF}/\overline{FB}) = \pm 1.$$

That the sign must be + follows from the fact that either none or two of the points D, E, F divide their corresponding sides externally.

Sufficiency: Suppose that

$$(\overline{BD}/\overline{DC})(\overline{CE}/\overline{EA})(\overline{AF}/\overline{FB}) = + 1$$

and let BE, CF intersect in P and draw AP to cut BC in D'. Then AD' is a cevian line. Hence, by the above, we have

$$(\overline{BD'}/\overline{D'C})(\overline{CE}/\overline{EA})(\overline{AF}/\overline{FB}) = + 1.$$

It follows that $\overline{BD'}/\overline{D'C} = \overline{BD}/\overline{DC}$, or that $D \equiv D'$. That is, AD, BE, CF are concurrent.

   2.3.6   *Trigonometric Form of Ceva's Theorem.   A necessary and sufficient condition for three cevian lines* AD, BE, CF *of an ordinary triangle* ABC *to be concurrent is that*

$$(\sin \overline{BAD}/\sin \overline{DAC})(\sin \overline{CBE}/\sin \overline{EBA})(\sin \overline{ACF}/\sin \overline{FCB}) = + 1.$$

The reader can easily supply a proof similar to that given for Theorem 2.3.3.

We illustrate the power of the theorems of Menelaus and Ceva by now using them to establish three useful and highly attractive theorems. Many further illustrations will be found among the problems at the end of this section.

2.3.7 *Theorem.* *If* AD, BE, CF *are any three concurrent cevian lines of an ordinary triangle* ABC, *and if* D' *denotes the point of intersection of* BC *and* FE, *then* D *and* D' *divide* BC, *one internally and one externally, in the same numerical ratio.*

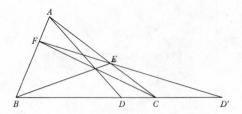

Fig. 2.3c

Since *AD*, *BE*, *CF* are concurrent cevian lines (see Fig. 2.3c) we have, by Ceva's Theorem,

$$(\overline{BD}/\overline{DC})(\overline{CE}/\overline{EA})(\overline{AF}/\overline{FB}) = +1.$$

Since *D'*, *E*, *F* are collinear menelaus points we have, by Menelaus' Theorem,

$$(\overline{BD'}/\overline{D'C})(\overline{CE}/\overline{EA})(\overline{AF}/\overline{FB}) = -1.$$

It follows that

$$\overline{BD}/\overline{DC} = -\overline{BD'}/\overline{D'C},$$

whence *D* and *D'* divide *BC*, one internally and one externally, in the same numerical ratio.

2.3.8 *Definitions.* Two triangles *ABC* and *A'B'C'* are said to be *copolar* if *AA'*, *BB'*, *CC'* are concurrent; they are said to be *coaxial* if the points of intersection of *BC* and *B'C'*, *CA* and *C'A'*, *AB* and *A'B'* are collinear.

2.3.9 *Desargues' Two-Triangle Theorem.* *Copolar triangles are coaxial, and conversely.*

Let the two triangles (see Fig. 2.3d) be *ABC* and *A'B'C'*. Suppose that *AA'*, *BB'*, *CC'* are concurrent in a point *O*. Let *P*, *Q*, *R* be the points of intersection of *BC* and *B'C'*, *CA* and *C'A'*, *AB* and *A'B'*. Considering the triangles *BCO*, *CAO*, *ABO* in turn, with the respective transversals *B'C'P,*, *C'A'Q,*, *A'B'R*, we find, by Menelaus' Theorem,

$$(\overline{BP}/\overline{PC})(\overline{CC'}/\overline{C'O})(\overline{OB'}/\overline{B'B}) = -1,$$

$$(\overline{CQ}/\overline{QA})(\overline{AA'}/\overline{A'O})(\overline{OC'}/\overline{C'C}) = -1,$$

$$(\overline{AR}/\overline{RB})(\overline{BB'}/\overline{B'O})(\overline{OA'}/\overline{A'A}) = -1.$$

Setting the product of the three left members of the above equations equal to the product of the three right members, we obtain

$$(\overline{BP}/\overline{PC})(\overline{CQ}/\overline{QA})(\overline{AR}/\overline{RB}) = -1,$$

whence P, Q, R are collinear. Thus copolar triangles are coaxial.

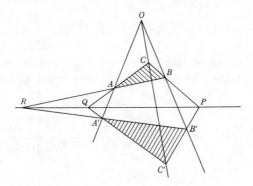

Fig. 2.3d

Conversely, suppose that P, Q, R are collinear and let O be the point of intersection of AA' and BB'. Now triangles AQA' and BPB' are copolar, and therefore coaxial. That is, O, C, C' are collinear. Thus, coaxial triangles are copolar.

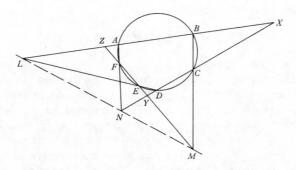

Fig. 2.3e

2.3.10 *Pascal's "Mystic-Hexagram" Theorem for a Circle.* *The points* L, M, N *of intersection of the three pairs of opposite sides* AB *and* DE, BC *and* EF, FA *and* CD *of a (not necessarily convex) hexagon* ABCDEF *inscribed in a circle lie on a line, called the* Pascal line *of the hexagon.*

Let X, Y, Z (see Fig. 2.3e) be the points of intersection of *AB* and *CD*, *CD* and *EF*, *EF* and *AB*, and consider *DE*, *FA*, *BC* as transversals cutting the sides of triangle *XYZ*. By the Theorem of Menelaus we have

$$(\overline{XL}/\overline{LZ})(\overline{ZE}/\overline{EY})(\overline{YD}/\overline{DX}) = -1,$$
$$(\overline{XA}/\overline{AZ})(\overline{ZF}/\overline{FY})(\overline{YN}/\overline{NX}) = -1,$$
$$(\overline{XB}/\overline{BZ})(\overline{ZM}/\overline{MY})(\overline{YC}/\overline{CX}) = -1.$$

Setting the product of the three left members of the above equations equal to the product of the three right members, and rearranging the ratios, we obtain

$$\left(\frac{\overline{XL}}{\overline{LZ}} \cdot \frac{\overline{ZM}}{\overline{MY}} \cdot \frac{\overline{YN}}{\overline{NX}}\right)\left(\frac{\overline{XB} \cdot \overline{XA}}{\overline{XC} \cdot \overline{XD}}\right)\left(\frac{\overline{YC} \cdot \overline{YD}}{\overline{YE} \cdot \overline{YF}}\right)\left(\frac{\overline{ZE} \cdot \overline{ZF}}{\overline{ZB} \cdot \overline{ZA}}\right) = -1. \tag{2.1}$$

But

$$\overline{XB} \cdot \overline{XA} = \overline{XC} \cdot \overline{XD},$$
$$\overline{YC} \cdot \overline{YD} = \overline{YE} \cdot \overline{YF},$$
$$\overline{ZE} \cdot \overline{ZF} = \overline{ZB} \cdot \overline{ZA},$$

whence each of the last three factors in parentheses in Eq. (2.1) has the value 1. It follows that

$$(\overline{XL}/\overline{LZ})(\overline{ZM}/\overline{MY})(\overline{YN}/\overline{NX}) = -1.$$

or *L, M, N* are collinear.

Desargues' two-triangle theorem appears to have been given by Desargues in a work on perspective in 1636, three years before his *Brouillon projet* was published. This theorem has become basic in the present-day theory of projective geometry, and we shall meet it again in later chapters. In deeper work one encounters so-called *non-Desarguesian geometries,* or plane geometries in which the two-triangle theorem fails to hold. The great French geometer

Jean-Victor Poncelet (1788-1867) made Desargues' two-triangle theorem the foundation of his theory of homologic figures.

Blaise Pascal (1623-1662) was inspired by the work of Desargues and was in possession of his "mystic-hexagram" theorem for a general conic when he was only 16 years old. The consequences of the "mystic-hexagram" theorem are very numerous and attractive, and an almost unbelievable amount of research has been expended on the configuration. A large number of different proofs have been supplied for the theorem itself. Some of these alternative proofs will be met in later parts of the book.

PROBLEMS

2.3-1   Supply a proof of Theorem 2.3.6.

2.3-2   Using Ceva's Theorem prove that: (a) The medians of a triangle are concurrent. (b) The internal angle bisectors of a triangle are concurrent. (c) The altitudes of a triangle are concurrent.

2.3-3   If D, E, F are the points of contact of the inscribed circle of triangle ABC with the sides BC, CA, AB, respectively, show that AD, BE, CF are concurrent. (This point of concurrency is called the *Gergonne point* of the triangle, after J. D. Gergonne (1771-1859), founder-editor of the mathematics journal *Annales de mathématiques*. Just why the point was named after Gergonne seems not to be known.)

2.3-4   Let D, E, F be the points on the sides BC, CA, AB of triangle ABC such that D is halfway around the perimeter from A, E halfway around from B, and F halfway around from C. Show that AD, BE, CF are concurrent. (This point of concurrency is called the *Nagel point* of the triangle, after C. H. Nagel (1803–1882), who considered it in a work of 1836.)

2.3-5   Let X and X' be points on a line segment MN symmetric with respect to the midpoint of MN. Then X and X' are called a pair of *isotomic points* for the segment MN. Show that if D and D', E and E', F and F' are isotomic points for the sides BC, CA, AB of triangle ABC, and if AD, BE, CF are concurrent, then AD', BE', CF' are also concurrent. (Two such related points of concurrency are called a pair of *isotomic conjugate. points* for the triangle, a term introduced by John Casey in 1889.)

2.3-6   Show that the Gergonne and Nagel points of a triangle are a pair of isotomic conjugate points for the triangle. (See Problems 2.3-3, 2.3-4, 2.3-5 for the required definitions.)

2.3-7   If, in Problem 2.3-5, D, E, F are collinear, show that D', E', F' are also collinear. (Two such related lines as DEF and $D'E'F'$ are sometimes called a pair of *reciprocal transversals* of the triangle ABC, a name used by G. de Longchamps in 1890.)

2.3-8   Let OX or OX' be rays through vertex O of angle MON symmetric with respect to the bisector of angle MON. Then OX and OX' are called a pair of *isogonal lines* for the angle MON. Show that if AD and AD', BE and BE', CF and CF' are isogonal cevian lines for the angles A, B, C of a triangle ABC, and if AD, BE, CF are concurrent, then AD', BE', CF' are also concurrent. (This theorem was proved by Jacob Steiner in 1828, and was extended to three-space by J. Neuberg in 1884. Two such related points of concurrency are called a pair of *isogonal conjugate points* for the triangle. The orthocenter and circumcenter of a triangle are a pair of isogonal conjugate points. The incenter is its own isogonal conjugate. The isogonal conjugate of the centroid is called the *symmedian point* of the triangle; it enjoys some very attractive properties.)

2.3-9   If, in Problem 2.3-8, D, E, F are collinear, show that D', E', F' are also collinear.

2.3-10   Let AD, BE, CF be three concurrent cevian lines of triangle ABC, and let the circle through D, E, F intersect the sides BC, CA, AB again in D', E', F'. Show that AD', BE', CF' are concurrent.

2.3-11   Show that the tangents to the circumcircle of a triangle at the vertices of the triangle intersect the opposite sides of the triangle in three collinear points.

2.3-12   If AD, BE, CF are three cevian lines of an ordinary triangle ABC, concurrent in a point P, and if DE, EF, FD intersect the sides BC, CA, AB of triangle ABC in the points D', E', F', show that D', E', F' are collinear on a line p. (J. J. A. Mathieu, in 1865, called the point P the *trilinear pole* of the line p, and the line p the *trilinear polar* of the point P, for the triangle ABC. The trilinear polar of the orthocenter of a triangle is called the *orthic axis* of the triangle.)

2.3-13   Prove that the external bisectors of the angles of a triangle intersect the opposite sides in three collinear points.

2.3-14   Prove that two internal angle bisectors and the external bisector of the third angle of a triangle intersect the opposite sides in three collinear points.

2.3-15   Establish the necessity part of Ceva's Theorem by applying Menelaus' Theorem to triangles ABD and ADC (of Fig. 2.3b) with transversals CF and BE, respectively.

2.3-16   If equilateral triangles BCA', CAB', ABC' are described externally upon the sides BC, CA, AB of triangle ABC, show that AA', BB', CC' are concurrent in a point P. (The point P is the first notable point of the triangle discovered after Greek times. If the angles of triangle ABC are each less than $120°$, then P is the point the sum of whose distances from A, B, C is a minimum. The minimization problem was proposed to Torricelli by Fermat. Torricelli solved the problem and his solution was published in 1659 by his student Viviani.)

2.3-17   Show that, in Problem 2.3-16, AA', BB', CC' are still concurrent if the equilateral triangles are described internally upon the sides of the given triangle ABC. (The two points of concurrency of Problems 2.3-16 and 2.3-17 are known as the *isogonic centers* of triangle ABC. The isogonal conjugates of the isogonic centers are called the *isodynamic points* of the triangle, a term given by J. Neuberg in 1885.)

2.3-18   Let D', E', F' be menelaus points on the sides $B'C', C'A', A'B'$ of triangle $A'B'C'$ and let O be a point not in the plane of $A'B'C'$. Show that D', E', F' are collinear if and only if

$$(\sin \overline{B'OD'}/\sin \overline{D'OC'})(\sin \overline{C'OE'}/\sin \overline{E'OA'})(\sin \overline{A'OF'}/\sin \overline{F'OB'})$$
$$= -1.$$

2.3-19   Let D, E, F be three menelaus points on the sides BC, CA, AB of a spherical triangle ABC. Show that D, E, F lie on a great circle of the sphere if and only if

$$(\sin \widehat{BD}/\sin \widehat{DC})(\sin \widehat{CE}/\sin \widehat{EA})(\sin \widehat{AF}/\sin \widehat{FB}) = -1.$$

2.3-20   If the lines joining a point O to the vertices of a polygon $ABCD \cdots$ of an odd number of sides meet the opposite sides

$AB, BC, CD, DE, \cdots$ in the points $A', B', C', D', \cdots$, show that

$$(\overline{AA'} / \overline{A'B})(\overline{BB'} / \overline{B'C})(\overline{CC'} / \overline{C'D})(\overline{DD'} / \overline{D'E}) \cdots = 1.$$

(This is a generalization of Ceva's Theorem.)

2.3-21 If a transversal cuts the sides $AB, BC, CD, DE, \cdots$ of an n-gon $ABCDE \cdots$ in the points $A', B', C', D', \cdots$ show that

$$(\overline{AA'} / \overline{A'B})(\overline{BB'} / \overline{B'C})(\overline{CC'} / \overline{C'D})(\overline{DD'} / \overline{D'E}) \cdots = (-1)^n.$$

(This is a generalization of Menelaus' Theorem.)

2.4 CROSS RATIO

Another topic which originated with the ancient Greeks, and of which certain aspects were very fully investigated by them, is that now called "cross ratio." In the nineteenth century this concept was revived and considerably improved with the aid of sensed magnitudes and with a highly convenient notation rendered possible by sensed magnitudes. The modern development of the subject is due, independently of each other, to Möbius (in his *Der barycentrische Calcul* of 1827) and Michel Chasles (in his *Aperçu historique sur l'origine et le développement des méthods en géométrie* of 1829–1837, his *Traité de géométrie supérieure* of 1852, and his *Traité des sections coniques* of 1865). A treatment of the cross-ratio concept freed of metrical considerations was made by Carl George von Staudt (in his *Beiträge zur Geometrie der Lage* of 1847). The cross-ratio concept has become basic in projective geometry, where its power and applicability are of prime importance.

2.4.1 *Definition and Notation.* If A, B, C, D are four distinct points on an ordinary line, we designate the ratio of ratios

$$(\overline{AC} / \overline{CB}) / (\overline{AD} / \overline{DB})$$

by the symbol (AB, CD), and call it the *cross ratio* (or *anharmonic ratio*, or *double ratio*) of the range of points A, B, C, D, taken in this order.

Essentially the notation (AB, CD) was introduced by Möbius in 1827. He employed the term *Doppelschnitt-Verhältniss*, and this was later abbreviated by Jacob Steiner to *Doppelverhältniss*, the English equivalent of which is *double ratio*. Chasles used the expression *rapport anharmonique* (*anharmonic ratio*) in 1837, and William Kingdon Clifford coined the term *cross ratio* in 1878. Staudt used the term *Wurf* (*throw*).

The cross ratio of four collinear points depends upon the order in which the points are selected. Since there are twenty-four permutations of four distinct objects, there are twenty-four ways in which a cross ratio of four distinct collinear points may be written. These cross ratios, however, are not all different in value. In fact, we proceed to show that the twenty-four cross ratios may be arranged into six sets of four each, such that the cross ratios in each set have the same value. Indeed, if one of these values be denoted by r, the others are $1/r$, $1 - r$, $1/(1 - r)$, $(r - 1)/r$, and $r/(r - 1)$.

2.4.2   *Theorem. If, in the symbol* (AB,CD) = r *for the cross ratio of four distinct points,* (1) *we interchange any two of the points and at the same time interchange the other two points, the cross ratio is unaltered,* (2) *we interchange only the first pair of points, the resulting cross ratio is* $1/r$, (3) *we interchange only the middle pair of points, the resulting cross ratio is* $1 - r$.

For the first part we must show that

$$(BA,DC) = (CD,AB) = (DC,BA) = (AB,CD) = r,$$

which is easily accomplished by expanding each of the involved cross ratios.

For the second part we must show that

$$(BA,CD) = 1/r,$$

and this too is easily accomplished by expansion.

For the third part we must show that

$$(AC,BD) = 1 - r.$$

This may be accomplished neatly by dividing the Euler identity (Theorem 2.1.5)

$$\overline{AD} \cdot \overline{BC} + \overline{BD} \cdot \overline{CA} + \overline{CD} \cdot \overline{AB} = 0$$

by $\overline{AD} \cdot \overline{BC}$, obtaining

$$1 + (\overline{BD} \cdot \overline{CA})/(\overline{AD} \cdot \overline{BC}) + (\overline{CD} \cdot \overline{AB})/(\overline{AD} \cdot \overline{BC}) = 0,$$

or, rearranging,

$$(\overline{AB}/\overline{BC})/(\overline{AD}/\overline{DC}) = 1 - (\overline{AC}/\overline{CB})/(\overline{AD}/\overline{DB}),$$

whence $(AC,BD) = 1 - (AB,CD)$.

   2.4.3   *Theorem.*   *If* (AB,CD) = r, *then*

(1)	(AB,CD)	= (BA,DC)	= (CD,AB)	= (DC,BA)	= r,
(2)	(BA,CD)	= (AB,DC)	= (DC,AB)	= (CD,BA)	= 1/r,
(3)	(AC,BD)	= (BD,AC)	= (CA,DB)	= (DB,CA)	= 1 - r,
(4)	(CA,BD)	= (DB,AC)	= (AC,DB)	= (BD,CA)	= 1/(1 - r),
(5)	(BC,AD)	= (AD,BC)	= (DA,CB)	= (CB,DA)	= (r - 1)/r,
(6)	(CB,AD)	= (DA,BC)	= (AD,CB)	= (BC,DA)	= r/(r - 1).

The equalities (1) are guaranteed by the first part of Theorem 2.4.2. The equalities (2) are obtained from those in (1) by applying the operation of the second part of Theorem 2.4.2; the equalities (3) are obtained from those in (1) by applying the operation of the third part of Theorem 2.4.2; the equalities (4) are obtained from those in (3) by applying the operation of the second part of Theorem 2.4.2; the equalities (5) are obtained from those in (2) by applying the operation of the third part of Theorem 2.4.2; the equalities (6) are obtained from those in (5) by applying the operation of the second part of Theorem 2.4.2.

   2.4.4   *Definition and Notation.*   If VA, VB, VC, VD are four distinct coplanar lines passing through an ordinary point V, we designate the ratio of ratios

$$(\sin \overline{AVC}/\sin \overline{CVB})/(\sin \overline{AVD}/\sin \overline{DVB})$$

by the symbol V(AB,CD), and call it the *cross ratio* of the pencil of lines VA, VB, VC, VD, taken in this order. It is to be observed (see Theorem 2.1.10) that this definition is independent of the positions of the points A, B, C, D on their respective lines, so long as they are distinct from V.

   2.4.5   *Theorem.*   *If four distinct parallel lines* a, b, c, d *are cut by two transversals in the points* A, B, C, D *and* A', B', C', D', *respectively, then* (AB,CD) = (A'B',C'D').

This follows immediately from the fact that the segments cut off by the parallel lines on one transversal are proportional to the corresponding segments cut off on the other transversal.

   2.4.6   *Definition.*   The *cross ratio* of a pencil of four distinct parallel lines *a, b, c, d* is taken to be the cross ratio of the range A, B, C, D cut off by the parallel lines on any transversal to these lines.

We now state and prove the theorem which gives to cross ratio its singular power in projective geometry.

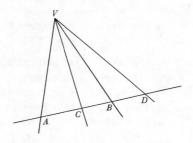

2.4.7   *Theorem.*   *The cross ratio of any pencil of four distinct lines is equal to the cross ratio of the corresponding four points in which any ordinary transversal cuts the pencil.*

If the vertex of the pencil is a point at infinity, the theorem follows from Definition 2.4.6.

Suppose that the vertex V of the pencil is not at infinity, and let A, B, C, D be the points in which the pencil is cut by an ordinary transversal (see Fig. 2.4a). Then, by Theorem 2.1.9,

$$\overline{AC}/\overline{CB} = (VA \ \sin \ \overline{AVC})/(VB \ \sin \ \overline{DVB}),$$

$$\overline{AD}/\overline{DB} = (VA \ \sin \ \overline{AVD})/(VB \ \sin \ \overline{DVB}),$$

whence

$$(\overline{AC}/\overline{CB})/(\overline{AD}/\overline{DB}) = (\sin \ \overline{AVC}/\sin \ \overline{CVB})/(\sin \ \overline{AVD}/\sin \ \overline{DVB}).$$

It follows that (AB,CD), $= V(AB,CD)$, and the theorem is established.

We now state two useful corollaries to Theorem 2.4.7. The proofs can easily be supplied by the reader.

2.4.8   *Corollary.   If* A, B, C, D *and* A′, B′, C′, D′ *are two coplanar ranges on distinct bases such that*   (AB,CD) = (A′B′,C′D′),   *and if* A *and* A′ *coincide, then* BB′, CC′, DD′ *are concurrent.*

2.4.9   *Corollary.   If* VA, VB, VC, VD *and* V′A, V′B, V′C, V′D *are two coplanar pencils on distinct vertices* V *and* V′ *such that* V(AB,CD) = V′(AB,CD), *and if* A *lies on* VV′, *then* B, C, D *are collinear.*

The next theorem, which is an immediate consequence of the

elementary angle relations in a circle, gives an important cross-ratio property of the circle.

2.4.10   *Theorem.   If* A, B, C, D *are any four distinct points on a circle, and if* V *and* V' *are any two points on the circle, then* V(AB,CD) = V'(AB,CD), *where* VA, *say, is taken as the tangent to the circle at* A *if* V *should coincide with* A.

We now illustrate the power of cross ratio by proving anew Desargues' two-triangle theorem (Theorem 2.3.9) and Pascal's "mystic-hexagram" theorem for a circle (Theorem 2.3.10). Further illustrations will be found among the problems at the end of this section and in various other parts of the book.

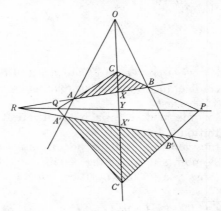

Fig. 2.4b

2.4.11   *Desargues' Two-Triangle Theorem.   Copolar triangles are co-axial, and conversely.*

Let the two triangles (see Fig. 2.4b) be ABC and $A'B'C'$. Suppose that AA', BB', CC' are concurrent in a point O. Let P, Q, R be the points of intersection of BC and $B'C'$, CA and $C'A'$, AB and $A'B'$. Let CC' cut AB in X, $A'B'$ in X', and PQ in Y. Then, by successive applications of Theorem 2.4.7

$$C(YP,QR) = (XB,AR) = O(XB,AR) = (X'B',A'R)$$
$$\overline{} = C'(X'B',\overline{A}'R) = C'(YP,QR).$$

Since Y lies on CC', it follows (by Corollary 2.4.9) that P, Q, R are collinear.

Conversely, suppose that P, Q, R are collinear. Then, again by successive applications of Theorem 2.4.7,

$$(RA,XB) = C(RA,XB) = C(RQ,YP) = C'(RQ,YP) = (RA',X'B').$$

It now follows (by Corollary 2.4.8) that AA', XX' (or CC'), BB' are concurrent.

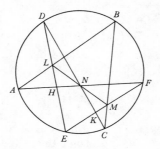

Fig. 2.4c

2.4.12 *Pascal's "Mystic-Hexagram" Theorem for a Circle. The points* L, M, N *of intersection of the three pairs of opposite sides* AB *and* DE. BC *and* EF, FA *and* CD *of a (not necessarily convex) hexagon* ABCDEF *inscribed in a circle lie on a line.*

Let AF and ED (see Fig. 2.4c) intersect in H, and EF and CD in K. Then (by Theorem 2.4.10) $A(EB,DF) = C(EB,DF)$, whence (by Theorem 2.4.7) $(EL,DH) = (EM,KF)$. It now follows (by Corollary 2.4.8) that LM, DK, HF are concurrent, or that L,M,N are collinear.

PROBLEMS

2.4-1 Supply proofs for Corollaries 2.4.8 and 2.4.9.

2.4-2 Prove Theorem 2.4.10.

2.4-3 If A, B, C, D are four distinct collinear points, show that the pairs A, B and C, D do or do not separate each other according as (AB,CD) is negative or positive.

2.4-4 Given three distinct points A, B, C on a line l, construct a fourth point D collinear with them such that (AB,CD) shall have a given value r.

2.4-5 Let a, b, c, d be four distinct fixed tangents to a given circle and let p be a variable fifth tangent. If p cuts a, b, c, d in A, B, C, D, show that (AB,CD) is a constant independent of the position of p.

2.4-6   Prove Brianchon's Theorem for a circle: If $ABCDEF$ is a (not necessarily convex) hexagon circumscribed about a circle, then AD, BE, CF are concurrent.

2.4-7   If P, Q, R, S, T are collinear points, show that:
(a) $(PQ,RT)(PQ,TS) = (PQ,RS)$.
(b) $(PT,RS)(TQ,RS) = (PQ,RS)$.

2.4-8   If two transversals cut the sides BC, CA, AB of a triangle ABC in points P, Q, R and P', Q', R', show that

$$(BC,PP')(CA,QQ')(AB,RR') = 1.$$

2.4-9   Prove Pappus' Theorem: If A, C, E and B, D, F are two sets of three points on distinct lines, then the points of intersection of AB and DE, BC and EF, FA and CD are collinear.

2.5   HARMONIC DIVISION

Very important and particularly useful is the special cross ratio having the value -1. Since, as we shall see, there is an intimate connection between such a cross ratio and three numbers in harmonic progression, such a cross ratio is referred to as a "harmonic division."

2.5.1   *Definitions.* If A, B, C, D are four collinear points such that $(AB,CD) = -1$ (so that C and D divide AB one internally and the other externally in the same numerical ratio), the segment AB is said to be *divided harmonically* by C and D, the points C and D are called *harmonic conjugates* of each other with respect to A and B, and the four points A, B, C, D are said to constitute a *harmonic range.* If $V(AB,CD) = -1$, then VA, VB, VC, VD are said to constitute a *harmonic pencil.*

2.5.2   *Theorem.   If C and D divide AB harmonically, then A and B divide CD harmonically.*

For if $(AB,CD) = -1$, then (by Theorem 2.4.2(1)) so also does $(CD,AB) = -1$.

2.5.3   *Theorem.   The harmonic conjugate with respect to A and B of the midpoint of AB is the point at infinity on AB.*

Let M be the midpoint of AB. Then $\overline{AM}/\overline{MB} = 1$. It follows that if D is the harmonic conjugate of M with respect to A and B we must have $\overline{AD}/\overline{DB} = -1$. Thus (see Definition 2.2.3) D is the point at infinity on line AB.

The next two theorems furnish useful criteria for four collinear points to form a harmonic range.

2.5.4   *Theorem.*   (AB,CD) = - 1 *if and only if* $2/\overline{AB} = 1/\overline{AC} + 1/\overline{AD}$.
Suppose   that $(AB,CD) = -1$.   Then $\overline{AC}/\overline{CB} = -\overline{AD}/\overline{DB}$, whence

$$\overline{CB}/(\overline{AB}\cdot\overline{AC}) = \overline{BD}/(\overline{AB}\cdot\overline{AD}),$$

or

$$(\overline{AB}-\overline{AC})/(\overline{AB}\cdot\overline{AC}) = (\overline{AD}-\overline{AB})/(\overline{AB}\cdot\overline{AD}).$$

That is,

$$1/\overline{AC} - 1/\overline{AB} = 1/\overline{AB} - 1/\overline{AD},$$

or

$$2/\overline{AB} = 1/\overline{AC} + 1/\overline{AD}.$$

The converse may be established by reversing the above steps.

2.5.5   *Theorem.*   (AB,CD) = - 1 *if and only if* $\overline{OB}^2 = \overline{OC}\cdot\overline{OD}$, *where* O *is the midpoint of* AB.

Suppose   that $(AB,CD) = -1$.   Then $\overline{AC}/\overline{CB} = -\overline{AD}/\overline{DB}$, whence

$$(\overline{OC}-\overline{OA})/(\overline{OB}-\overline{OC}) = -(\overline{OD}-\overline{OA})/(\overline{OB}-\overline{OD}),$$

or, since $\overline{OA} = -\overline{OB}$,

$$(\overline{OC}+\overline{OB})/(\overline{OB}-\overline{OC}) = (\overline{OD}+\overline{OB})/(\overline{OD}-\overline{OB}).$$

It now follows that

$$(\overline{OC}+\overline{OB})(\overline{OD}-\overline{OB}) = (\overline{OD}+\overline{OB})(\overline{OB}-\overline{OC}).$$

or, upon multiplying out and simplifying,

$$\overline{OB}^2 = \overline{OC}\cdot\overline{OD}.$$

The converse may be established by reversing the above steps.

We now look at the connection between "harmonic division" and "harmonic progression."

2.5.6   *Definition.*   The   sequence   of   numbers $\{a_1, a_2, \cdots, a_n\}$

is said to be a *harmonic progression* if the sequence of numbers $\{1/a_1,\ 1/a_2,\ \cdots,\ 1/a_n\}$ is an arithmetic progression.

2.5.7 *Theorem.* *The sequence of numbers* $\{a_1,\ a_2,\ a_3\}$ *is a harmonic progression if and only if* $2/a_2\ =\ 1/a_1\ +\ 1/a_3$.

The proof follows readily from Definition 2.5.6.

2.5.8 *Theorem.* *If* $(AB,CD)\ =\ -1$, *then* $\{\overline{AC},\ \overline{AB},\ \overline{AD}\}$ *is a harmonic progression.*

This is a consequence of Theorems 2.5.4 and 2.5.7.

We conclude this section with a brief consideration of complete quadrilaterals and complete quadrangles, and their useful harmonic properties.

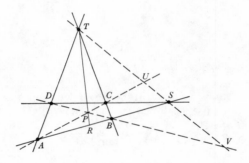

Fig. 2.5a

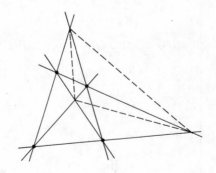

Fig. 2.5b

2.5.9 *Definitions.* A *complete quadrilateral* (see Fig. 2.5a) is the figure formed by four coplanar lines no three of which are concurrent. The four lines are called the *sides* of the complete quadrilateral, and the six points of intersection of pairs of the sides are called the *vertices* of the complete quadrilateral. Pairs of vertices not lying on any common side are called *opposite vertices* of the complete quadrilateral. The lines through the three pairs of opposite vertices are called the *diagonal lines* of the complete quadrilateral, and the triangle determined by the three diagonal lines is called the *diagonal 3-line* of the complete quadrilateral.

A *complete quadrangle* (see Fig. 2.5b) is the figure formed by four coplanar points no three of which are collinear. The four points are called the *vertices* of the complete quadrangle, and the six lines determined by pairs of the vertices are called the *sides* of the complete quadrangle. Pairs of sides not passing through any common vertex are called *opposite sides* of the complete quadrangle. The points of intersection of the three pairs of opposite sides are called the *diagonal points* of the complete quadrangle, and the triangle determined by the three diagonal points is called the *diagonal 3-point* of the complete quadrangle.

2.5.10   *Theorem.   On each diagonal line of a complete quadrilateral there is a harmonic range consisting of the two vertices of the quadrilateral and the two vertices of the diagonal 3-line lying on it.*

Let us show (see Fig. 2.5a) that $(UV, TS) = -1$. We have

$$(UV,TS) = P(UV,TS) = P(AB,RS) = (AB,RS).$$

But, by Theorem 2.3.7, $(AB,RS) = -1$. We may now easily show that $(PU,AC) = (PV,DB) = (UV,TS) = -1$.

2.5.11   *Theorem.   At each diagonal point of a complete quadrangle there is a harmonic pencil consisting of the two sides of the quadrangle and the two sides of the diagonal 3-point passing through it.*

This follows immediately from Theorem 2.3.7.

PROBLEMS

2.5-1   Justify each of the following methods of constructing the harmonic conjugate D of a given point C with respect to a given segment AB.

(a)   Take any point P not on line AB and connect P to A, B, C. Through B draw the parallel to AP, cutting line PC in M, and on this parallel mark off $\overline{BN} = \overline{MB}$. Then PN cuts line AB in the sought point D.

(b)   Draw the circle on AB as diameter. If C lies between A and B, draw CT perpendicular to AB to cut the circle in T. Then the tangent to the circle at T cuts line AB in the sought point D. If C is not between A and B, draw one of the tangents

CT to the circle, T being the point of contact of the tangent. Then the sought point D is the foot of the perpendicular dropped from T on AB.

(c)　Connect any point P not on line AB with A, B, C. Through A draw any line (other than AB or AP) to cut PC and PB in M and N, respectively. Draw BM to cut PA in G. Now draw GN to cut line AB in the sought point D. (Note that this construction uses only a straightedge.)

2.5-2　If $(AB, CD) = -1$ and O and O' are the midpoints of AB and CD, respectively, show that $(OB)^2 + (O'C)^2 = (OO')^2$.

2.5-3　(a)　Show that the lines joining any point on a circle to the vertices of an inscribed square form a harmonic pencil.

(b)　Show, more generally, that the lines joining any point on a circle to the extremities of a given diameter and to the extremities of a given chord perpendicular to the diameter form a harmonic pencil.

(c)　Triangle ABC is inscribed in a circle of which DE is the diameter perpendicular to side AC. If lines DB and EB intersect AC in L and M, show that $(AC, LM) = -1$.

(d)　Show that the diameter of a circle perpendicular to one of the sides of an inscribed triangle is divided harmonically by the other two sides.

2.5-4　(a)　If L, M, N are the midpoints of the sides BC, CA, AB of a triangle ABC show that $L(MN, AB) = -1$.

(b)　If P, Q, R are the feet of the altitudes on sides BC, CA, AB of a triangle ABC, show that $P(QR, AB) = -1$.

(c)　The bisector of angle A of triangle ABC intersects the opposite side in T. U and V are the feet of the perpendiculars from B and C upon line AT. Show that $(AT, UV) = -1$.

2.5-5　Let BC be a diameter of a given circle, let A be a point on BC produced, and let P and Q be the points of contact of the tangent to the circle from point A. Show that $P(AQ, CB) = -1$.

2.5-6　If $P(AB, CD) = -1$ and if PC is perpendicular to PD, show that PC and PD are the bisectors of angle APB.

2.5-7　If O is any point on the altitude AP of triangle ABC, and BO and CO intersect AC and AB in E and F, respectively, show that PA bisects angle EPF.

2.5-8　In triangle ABC we have $(BC, PP') = (CA, QQ') = (AB, RR') = -1$. Show that AP', BQ', CR' are concurrent if and only if P, Q, R are collinear.

2.5-9   If $(AB, CD) = -1$ and O is the midpoint of CD, show that $\overline{AC} \cdot \overline{AD} = \overline{AB} \cdot \overline{AO}$.

2.5-10   If P, P' divide one diameter of a circle harmonically and Q, Q' divide another diameter harmonically, prove that P, Q, P', Q' are concyclic.

2.5-11   Two circles intersect in points A and B. A common tangent touches the circles at P and Q and cuts a third circle through A and B in L and M. Prove that $(PQ, LM) = -1$.

2.5-12   A circle Σ inscribed in a semicircle touches the diameter AB of the semicircle at a point C. Prove that the diameter of Σ is the harmonic mean between AC and CB.

2.5-13   In Fig. 2.5a, prove that UD, VA, PS are concurrent.

2.5-14   Prove that the geometric mean of two positive numbers is the geometric mean of the arithmetic mean and harmonic mean of the two numbers.

2.6   SOME MODERN ELEMENTARY GEOMETRY OF THE CIRCLE

For later purposes we shall need certain parts of the elementary geometry of circles that did not make their appearance until the nineteenth century. The material we are concerned about is that centered around the concepts of orthogonal circles, the power of a point with respect to a circle, the radical axis of a pair of circles, the radical center and radical circle of a trio of circles, and coaxial pencils of circles. Though one can see the notion of power of a point with respect to a circle foreshadowed in Propositions 35 and 36 of Book III of Euclid's *Elements*, the concept was first crystallized and developed by Louis Gaultier in a paper published in 1813 in the *Journal de l'École Polytechnique*. Here we find, for the first time, the terms *radical axis* and *radical center*; the term *power* was introduced somewhat later by Jacob Steiner. The initial studies of orthogonal circles and coaxial pencils of circles were made in the early nineteenth century by Gaultier, Poncelet, Steiner, J. B. Durrende, and others. This rather recent elementary geometry of the circle has found valuable application in various parts of mathematics and physics.

We start with a definition of orthogonal curves.

2.6.1   *Definitions.* By the *angles of intersection* of two coplanar curves at a point which they have in common is meant the angles between the tangents to the curves at the common point. If the angles of intersection are right angles, the two curves are said to be *orthogonal*.

The facts stated about circles in the following theorem are quite obvious.

2.6.2   *Theorem.* (1) *The angles of intersection at one of the common points of two intersecting circles are equal to those at the other common point.* (2) *If two circles are orthogonal, a radius of either, drawn to a point of intersection, is tangent to the other; conversely, if the radius of one of two intersecting circles, drawn to a point of intersection, is tangent to the other, the circles are orthogonal.* (3) *Two circles are orthogonal if and only if the square of the distance between their centers is equal to the sum of the squares of their radii.* (4) *If two circles are orthogonal, the center of each lies outside the other.*

We now establish a deeper fact about orthogonal circles that will be useful to us in a later chapter.

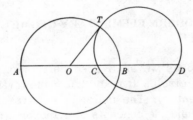

Fig. 2.6a

2.6.3   *Theorem.   If two circles are orthogonal, then any diameter of one which intersects the other is cut harmonically by the other; conversely, if a diameter of one circle is cut harmonically by a second circle, then the two circles are orthogonal.*

Let O (see Fig. 2.6a) be the center of one of a pair of orthogonal circles and let a diameter AOB of this circle cut the other in points C and D. Let T be a point of intersection of the two circles. Then $(OB)^2 = (OT)^2 = (\overline{OC})(\overline{OD})$, since (by Theorem 2.6.2 (2)) OT is tangent to the second circle. It now follows (by Theorem 2.5.5) that $(AB,CD) = -1$.

Conversely,   if $(AB,CD) = -1$,   then (by Theorem 2.5.5) $(OT)^2 = (OB)^2 = (\overline{OC})(\overline{OD})$,   and OT is tangent to the second circle, whence (by Theorem 2.6.2(2)) the two circles are orthogonal.

As mentioned earlier, Propositions III 35 and III 36 of Euclid's *Elements* contain the germs of the notion of power of a point with respect to a circle. With the aid of sensed magnitudes, these two propositions can be combined into the following single statement.

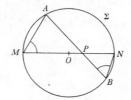

Fig. 2.6b₁

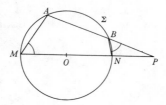

Fig. 2.6b₂

2.6.4   *Theorem.   If P is a fixed point in the plane of a given circle Σ, and if a variable line* l *through* P *intersects* Σ *in points* A *and* B, *then the product* $\overline{PA}$ · $\overline{PB}$ *is independent of the position of* l.

Let O be the center of Σ. If P coincides with O, or lies on Σ, or is an ideal point, the theorem is obvious. Otherwise (see Figs. 2.6b₁ and 2.6b₂), draw the diameter MN through the point P and connect A with M and B with N. The two triangles PMA and PBN are equiangular, and therefore similar, whence

$$\overline{PA}/\overline{PM} = \overline{PN}/\overline{PB} \quad \text{or} \quad \overline{PA} \cdot \overline{PB} = \overline{PM} \cdot \overline{PN}$$

and the theorem follows since the right-hand side of the last equality is independent of the position of l.

The preceding theorem justifies the following definition.

2.6.5   *Definition.*   The   *power of a point with respect to a circle*   is the product of the signed distances of the point from any two points on the circle and collinear with it.

It follows that the power of a point with respect to a circle is positive, zero, or negative according as the point lies outside, on, or inside the circle. If the point lies outside the circle, its power with respect to the circle is equal to the square of the tangent from the point to the circle; if the point lies inside the circle, its power with respect to the circle is the negative of the square of half the chord perpendicular to the diameter passing through the given point. We thus have:

2.6.6   *Theorem.   Let* P *be a point in the plane of a circle* Σ *of center* O *and radius* r. *The power of* P *with respect to* Σ *is equal to* $(OP)^2 - r^2$.

We leave it to the reader to show that Theorem 2.6.3 can be rephrased as follows:

2.6.7   *Theorem.   A necessary and sufficient condition for two circles to be orthogonal is that the power of the center of either with respect to the other be equal to the square of the corresponding radius.*

2.6.8   *Definition.*   The locus of a point whose powers with respect to two given circles are equal is called the *radical axis* of the two given circles.

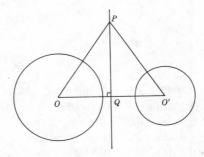

Fig. 2.6c

2.6.9   *Theorem.   The radical axis of two nonconcentric circles is a straight line perpendicular to the line of centers of the two circles.*

Consider two nonconcentric circles with centers O and O' and radii r and r' (see Fig. 2.6c), and let P be any point on the radical axis of the two circles. Let Q be the foot of the perpendicular from P to OO'. Then (by Theorem 2.6.6)

$$(PO)^2 - r^2 = (PO')^2 - r'^2.$$

Subtracting $(PQ)^2$ from each side we get

$$(OQ)^2 - r^2 = (QO')^2 - r'^2,$$

or

$$(\overline{OQ} + \overline{QO'})\,(\overline{OQ} - \overline{QO'}) = r^2 - r'^2.$$

whence

$$\overline{OQ} - \overline{QO'} = (r^2 - r'^2)\,/\,\overline{OO'}. \tag{2.2}$$

Now there is only one point Q on OO' satisfying relation (2.2). For if R is any such point we have

$$\overline{OQ} - \overline{QO'} = \overline{OR} - \overline{RO'},$$

or

$$(\overline{OR} + \overline{RQ}) - \overline{QO'} = \overline{OR} - (\overline{RQ} + \overline{QO'}),$$

or

$$\overline{OR} - \overline{QR} - \overline{QO'} = \overline{OR} + \overline{QR} - \overline{QO'},$$

and $\overline{QR} = 0$, or R coincides with Q. It follows that if a point is on the radical axis of the two circles it lies on the perpendicular to the line of centers at the point Q. Conversely, by reversing the above steps, it can be shown that any point on the perpendicular to OO' at Q lies on the radical axis of the two circles. Therefore the radical axis of the two circles is the perpendicular to OO' at the point Q.

2.6.10   *Remark.*   If, in equation (2.2) of the proof of Theorem 2.6.9, $r' \ne r$ and O' approaches O, Q approaches an ideal point. The radical axis of two unequal concentric circles is therefore frequently defined to be the line at infinity in the plane of the circles. The radical axis of two equal concentric circles is left undefined, and it is to be understood that any statement about radical axes is not intended to include this situation.

2.6.11   *Theorem.   The radical axes of three circles with noncollinear centers, taken in pairs, are concurrent.*

Let P be the intersection of the radical axis of the first and second circles with that of the second and third circles. Then P has equal powers with respect to all three circles, and thus must also lie on the radical axis of the first and third circles.

2.6.12   *Definition.*   The point of concurrence of the radical axes of three circles with noncollinear centers, taken in pairs, is called the *radical center* of the three circles.

2.6.13   *Theorem.*   (1) *The center of a circle which cuts each of two circles orthogonally lies on the radical axis of the two circles.* (2) *If a circle whose center lies on the radical axis of two circles is orthogonal to one of them, it is also orthogonal to the other.*

This is an immediate consequence of Theorem 2.6.7.

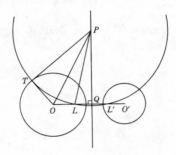

Fig. 2.6d$_1$

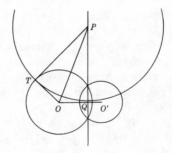

Fig. 2.6d$_2$

2.6.14   *Theorem.*   (1) *All the circles which cut each of two given non-intersecting circles orthogonally intersect the line of centers of the two given circles in the same two points.* (2) *A circle which cuts each of two given intersecting circles orthogonally does not intersect the line of centers of the two given circles.*

(1) Let a circle with center P cut two given circles with centers O and O' orthogonally. Then (by Theorem 2.6.13) P lies on the radical axis of the two given circles. Referring to Fig. 2.6d$_1$,

we then have $OQ > OT$, whence $PT > PQ$, and the common orthogonal circle intersects OO' in points L and L'. Now

$$(PL)^2 = (LQ)^2 + (QP)^2$$

and also

$$(PL)^2 = (PT)^2 = (PO)^2 - (OT)^2 = (OQ)^2 + (QP)^2 - (OT)^2,$$

whence

$$(LQ)^2 = (OQ)^2 - (OT)^2.$$

This last equation shows that the position of L is independent of that of P. Hence every circle orthogonal to the two given circles passes through point L. Similarly, every such circle passes through point L'.

(2) Referring to Fig. 2.6d$_2$ we have $OQ < OT$, whence $PT < PQ$, and the common orthogonal circle fails to intersect OO'.

2.6.15 *Definitions.*   A set of circles is said to form a *coaxial pencil* if the same straight line is the radical axis of any two circles of the set; the straight line is called the *radical axis* of the coaxial pencil.

Coaxial pencils of circles are very useful in certain mathematical and physical investigations. We leave to the reader the easy task of establishing the two following important theorems about such sets of circles.

2.6.16 *Theorem.*   (1) *The centers of the circles of a coaxial pencil are collinear.* (2) *If two circles of a coaxial pencil intersect, every circle of the pencil passes through the same two points; if two circles of a coaxial pencil are tangent at a point, all circles of the pencil are tangent to one another at the same point; if two circles of a coaxial pencil do not intersect, no two circles of the pencil intersect.* (3) *The radical axis of a coaxial pencil of circles is the locus of a point whose powers with respect to all the circles of the pencil are equal.*

2.6.17 *Definition.*   By Theorem 2.6.16 (2) there are three types of coaxial pencils of circles, and these are called an *intersecting coaxial pencil*, a *tangent coaxial pencil*, and a *nonintersecting coaxial pencil.*

2.6.18 *Theorem.*   (1) *All the circles orthogonal to two given nonintersecting circles belong to an intersecting coaxial pencil whose line of centers is the radical axis of the two given circles.* (2) *All the circles orthogonal to two given tangent circles belong to a tangent coaxial pencil whose line of centers is the common tangent to the two given circles.* (3) *All the circles orthogonal to two given intersecting circles belong to a nonintersecting coaxial pencil whose line of centers is the line of the common chord of the two given circles.*

We close the section with a particularly pretty application of some of the foregoing theory to the complete quadrilateral.

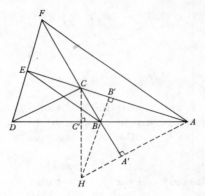

Fig. 2.6c

2.6.19 *Theorem. The three circles on the diagonals of a complete quadrilateral as diameters are coaxial; the orthocenters of the four triangles determined by the four sides of the quadrilateral taken three at a time are collinear; the midpoints of the three diagonals are collinear on a line perpendicular to the line of collinearity of the four orthocenters.*

Referring to Fig. 2.6e, let A, B, C, D, E, F be the six vertices of a complete quadrilateral, H the orthocenter of triangle ABC, and A', B', C' the feet of the altitudes of triangle ABC. Since A, C, C', A' and B', C, C', B are sets of concyclic points,

$$(\overline{HA})(\overline{HA'}) = (\overline{HB})(\overline{HB'}) = (\overline{HC})(\overline{HC'}).$$

But AA', BB', CC' are chords of the circles having the diagonals AF, BE, CD of the complete quadrilateral as diameters. It follows that H has the same power with respect to all three of these circles. Similarly it can be shown that the orthocenters of triangles ADE, BDF, CEF each have equal powers with respect to the three circles. It follows that the three circles are coaxial, the four orthocenters are collinear on their radical axis, and the centers of the circles (that is, the midpoints of the three diagonals) are collinear on a line perpendicular to the line of collinearity of the four orthocenters.

PROBLEMS

2.6-1   Establish Theorem 2.6.2.

2.6-2   Establish Theorem 2.6.7.

2.6-3   Show that if the radical center of three circles with noncollinear centers is exterior to each of the three circles, it is the center of a circle orthogonal to all three circles. (This circle is called the *radical circle* of the three circles.)

2.6-4   Establish Theorem 2.6.16.

2.6-5   Establish Theorem 2.6.18.

2.6-6   Prove that the radical axis of two circles having a common tangent bisects the segment on the common tangent determined by the points of contact.

2.6-7   Justify the following construction of the radical axis of two nonconcentric nonintersecting circles. Draw any circle cutting the given circles in A, A' and B, B', respectively. Through P, the intersection of AA' and BB', draw the perpendicular to the line of centers of the given circles. This perpendicular is the required radical axis.

2.6-8   Show that if d is the distance between the centers of two intersecting circles, c the length of their common chord, r and r' their radii, then the circles are orthogonal if and only if $cd = 2rr'$.

2.6-9   (a)   Prove that the radical center of the three circles constructed on the sides of a triangle as diameters is the orthocenter of the triangle.

(b)   Let AD, BE, CF be cevian lines of triangle ABC. Prove that the radical center of circles constructed on AD, BE, CF as diameters is the orthocenter of the triangle.

2.6-10   If the common chord of two intersecting circles C_1 and C_2 is a diameter of C_2, circle C_2 is said to be *bisected* by circle C_1, and circle C_1 is said to *bisect* circle C_2. Prove the following theorems concerning bisected circles.

(a)   If circle C_2 is bisected by circle C_1, the square of the radius of C_2 is equal to the negative of the power of the center of C_2 with respect to C_1.

(b)   If point P lies inside a circle C_1, then P is the center of a circle C_2 which is bisected by C_1.

(c)   If the radical center of three circles with noncollinear centers lies inside the three circles, then it is the center of a circle which is bisected by each of the three circles.

(d)   The locus of the center of a circle which bisects two given nonconcentric circles is a straight line parallel to the radical axis of the two given circles. (This line is called the *antiradical axis* of the two given circles.)

(e)   The circles having their centers on a fixed line and bisecting a given circle form a coaxial pencil of circles.

2.6-11   Prove that if each of a pair of circles cuts each of a second pair orthogonally, then the radical axis of either pair is the line of centers of the other.

2.6-12   (a)   Through a given point draw a circle that is orthogonal to two given circles.

(b)   Through a given point draw a circle that is coaxial with two given circles.

2.6-13   Show that there is one and only one straight line or circle orthogonal to a given circle Σ and passing through two given interior points A and B of Σ.

2.6-14   Show that there is one and only one straight line or circle orthogonal to a given circle Σ and having a given direction at a given interior point A of Σ.

III. ELEMENTARY
TRANSFORMATIONS

One of the most useful methods exploited by geometers of the modern era is that of cleverly transforming a figure into another which is better suited to a geometrical investigation. The gist of the idea is this. We wish to solve a difficult problem connected with a given figure. We *transform* the given figure into another which is related to it in a definite way and such that under the transformation the difficult problem concerning the original figure becomes a simpler problem concerning the new figure. We *solve* the simpler problem related to the new figure, and then *invert* the transformation to obtain the solution of the more difficult problem related to the original figure.

The idea of solving a difficult problem by means of an appropriate transformation is not peculiar to geometry but is found throughout mathematics. For example, if one were asked to find the Roman numeral representing the product of the two given Roman numerals LXIII and XXIV, one would *transform* the two given Roman numerals into the corresponding Hindu-Arabic numerals, 63 and 24, *solve* the related problem in the Hindu-Arabic notation by means of the familiar multiplication algorithm to obtain the product 1512, then *invert* this result back into Roman notation, finally obtaining MDXII as the answer to the original problem. By an appropriate transformation, a difficult problem has been converted into an easy problem.

Again, suppose we wish to show that the equation

$$x^7 - 2x^5 + 10x^2 - 1 = 0$$

has no root greater than 1. By the substitution $x = y + 1$ we *transform* the given equation into

$$y^7 + 7y^6 + 19y^5 + 25y^4 + 15y^3 + 11y^2 + 17y + 8 = 0.$$

Since the roots of this new equation are equal to the roots of the original equation diminished by 1 ($y = x - 1$), we must show that the new equation has no root greater than 0. We *solve* this problem simply by noting that all the coefficients in the new equation are positive, whence y cannot also be positive and yet yield a zero sum. Now if we *invert* the transformation we obtain the desired result.

Geometrical transformations, as indeed transformations in other areas of mathematics, are useful not only in solving problems, but also in discovering new facts. We *transform* a given figure into a new figure; by studying the new figure we *discover* some property of it; then we *invert* to obtain a property of the original figure. In this chapter we shall examine some elementary geometrical transformations that can frequently be used to simplify the solution of geometrical problems or to discover new geometrical facts. Applications of the *transform-solve-invert* and *transform-discover-invert* procedures will appear both in this chapter and, along with further transformations, in other parts of the book.

3.1 TRANSFORMATION THEORY

As an illustration of the principal concept to be introduced in this section, consider the set B of all books in some specific library and the set P of all positive integers. Let us associate with each book of the library the number of pages in the book. In this way we make correspond to each element of set B a unique element of set P, and we say that "the set B has been mapped into the set P." As another illustration, let N be the set of all names listed in some given telephone directory and let A be the set of twenty-six letters of the alphabet. Let us associate with each name in the directory the last letter of the surname, thus making correspond to each element of set N a unique element of set A. This correspondence defines "mapping of set N into set A." These are examples of the following formal definition.

3.1.1 *Definitions and Notation.* If A and B are two (not necessarily distinct) sets, then a *mapping* of set A into set B is a correspondence that associates with each element a of A a unique element b of B. We write $a \rightarrow b$, and call b the *image* (or *map*) of a under the mapping, and we say that element a has been *carried into* (or *mapped into*) element b by the mapping. If every element of B is the image of some element of A, then we say that set A has been mapped *onto* set B .

Thus if A is the set $\{1,2,3,4\}$ and B the set $\{a,b,c\}$, the associations

$$1 \rightarrow a, \; 2 \rightarrow b, \; 3 \rightarrow b, \; 4 \rightarrow a$$

define a mapping of set A into set B. This, however, is not a mapping of set A onto set B, since element c of B is not the image under the mapping of any element of set A. On the other hand, the mapping induced by the associations

$$1 \rightarrow a, \; 2 \rightarrow b, \; 3 \rightarrow b, \; 4 \rightarrow c$$

is a mapping of set A onto set B, for now every element of B is the unique image of some element of A.

3.1.2   *Definition.*   A mapping of a set A onto a set B in which distinct elements of A have distinct images in B is called a *transformation* (or *one-to-one mapping*) of A onto B .

3.1.3   *Definitions and Notation.*   If, in Definition 3.1.2, A and B are the same set, then the mapping is a transformation of a set A onto itself. In this case there may be an element of A which corresponds to itself. Such an element is called an *invariant element* (or *double element*) of the transformation. A transformation of a set A onto itself in which every element is an invariant element is called the *identity transformation* on A, and will, when no ambiguity is involved, be denoted by I.

3.1.4   *Definition and Notation.*   It is clear that a transformation of set A onto set B defines a second transformation, of set B onto set A, wherein an element of B is carried into the element of A of which it was the image under the first transformation. This second transformation is called the *inverse* of the first transformation. If T represents a transformation of a set A onto a set B, then the inverse transformation will be denoted by T^{-1}.

Thus if, among the married couples of a certain city, we let A be the set of husbands and B the set of wives, then the mapping which associates with each man of set A his wife in set B is a transformation of set A onto set B. The inverse of this transformation is the mapping of B onto A in which each woman in set B is associated with her husband in set A.

3.1.5 *Definitions and Notation.* Let T_1 be a transformation of set A onto set B and T_2 a transformation of set B onto set C. The performance of transformation T_1 followed by transformation T_2 induces a transformation T of set A onto set C, wherein an element a of A is associated with the element c of C which is the image under T_2 of the element b of B which is the image under T_1 of element a of A. Transformation T is called the *product* $T_2 T_1$ of transformations T_1 and T_2, taken in this order. If the product transformation $T_2 T_1$ exists, we say that T_2 is *compatible* with T_1.

Note that in the product $T_2 T_1$, transformation T_1 is to be performed first, then transformation T_2. That is, we perform the component transformations from *right to left*. This is purely a convention and we could, as some writers do, have agreed to write the product the other way about.

3.1.6 *Theorem.* *If* T_2 *is compatible with* T_1, *it does not follow that* T_1 *is compatible with* T_2. *If, however, both* T_1 *and* T_2 *are transformations of a set* A *onto itself, then necessarily both* T_2 *is compatible with* T_1 *and* T_1 *is compatible with* T_2.

The reader can easily construct an example where $T_2 T_1$ exists but $T_1 T_2$ does not exist. The second part of the theorem is quite obvious

3.1.7 *Definition and Notation.* Two transformations T_1 and T_2 of set A onto set B are said to be *equal*, and we write $T_1 = T_2$, if they are precisely the same mapping of A onto B.

3.1.8 *Definition.* A transformation T of a set A onto itself is said to be *involutoric* if $T^2 \equiv TT = I$.

3.1.9 *Theorem.* *A product of two compatible transformations, even if each is a transformation of a set* A *onto itself, is not necessarily commutative; that is, if* $T_1 T_2$ *and* $T_2 T_1$ *both exist, we do not necessarily have* $T_1 T_2 = T_2 T_1$.

Let A be the set of all points of a plane on which a rectangular coordinate framework has been superimposed. Let T_1 be the transformation of A onto itself which carries each point of A into a point one unit in the direction of the positive x axis, and let T_2 be the transformation of A onto itself which rotates each point of A counterclockwise about the origin through $90°$. Under $T_2 T_1$ the point $(1,0)$ is carried into the point $(0,2)$, whereas under $T_1 T_2$ it is carried into the point $(1,1)$. It follows that $T_1 T_2 \neq T_2 T_1$.

3.1.10 *Theorem.* *Multiplication of compatible transformations is associative; that is, if* T_1, T_2, T_3 *are transformations such that* T_2 *is compatible with* T_1 *and* T_3 *with* T_2, *then* $T_3 (T_2 T_1) = (T_3 T_2) T_1$.

For both $T_3(T_2 T_1)$ and $(T_3 T_2)T_1$ denote the resultant transformation obtained by first performing T_1, then T_2, then T_3.

We leave to the reader the establishment of the following three theorems.

3.1.11   *Theorem.   If* T *is a transformation of set* A *onto itself, then* (1) TI = IT = T, (2) $TT^{-1} = T^{-1}T = I$.

3.1.12   *Theorem.   If* T *and* S *are transformations of a set* A *onto itself, and if* TS = I, *then* S = T^{-1}.

3.1.13   *Theorem.   If transformation* T_2 *is compatible with transformation* T_1, *then* $(T_2 T_1)^{-1} = T_1^{-1} T_2^{-1}$.

PROBLEMS

3.1-1   If A represents the set of all integers, which of the following mappings of A into itself are mappings of A onto itself? Which are transformations of A onto itself?

(a) $a \to a + 5$ (d) $a \to 2a - 1$

(b) $a \to a + a^2$ (e) $a \to 5 - a$

(c) $a \to a^5$ (f) $a \to a - 5$

3.1-2   If R represents the set of all real numbers, which of the following mappings of R into itself are mappings of R onto itself? Which are transformations of R onto itself?

(a) $r \to 2r - 1$ (d) $r \to 1 - r$

(b) $r \to r^2$ (e) $r \to r + r^2$

(c) $r \to r^3$ (f) $r \to 5r$

3.1-3   If R represents the set of all real numbers, is the mapping indicated by the association $r \to r^3 - r$ a mapping of R onto itself? Is it a transformation of R onto itself?

3.1-4   (a)   Generalize Definition 3.1.5 for the situation where T_1 is a mapping of set A *into* set B and T_2 is a mapping of set B *into* set C.

(b)   Let T_1 and T_2 be the mappings of the set N of natural numbers into itself indicated by the associations $n \to n^2$ and $n \to 2n + 3$ respectively. Find the associations for the mappings $T_1 T_2$, $T_2 T_1$, T_1^2, T_2^2, $(T_1 T_2)T_1$, $T_1(T_2 T_1)$.

3.1-5   Supply a proof for Theorem 3.1.6.

3.1-6   Establish Theorem 3.1.11.

3.1-7   Establish Theorem 3.1.12.

3.1-8   Establish Theorem 3.1.13.

3.1-9   If T is a transformation of set A onto set B, show that $(T^{-1})^{-1} = T$.

3.1-10   If T is an involutoric transformation, show that $T = T^{-1}$.

3.1.11   If T_1, T_2, T_3 are transformations of a set A onto itself, show that $(T_3 T_2 T_1)^{-1} = T_1^{-1} T_2^{-1} T_3^{-1}$.

3.2   FUNDAMENTAL POINT TRANSFORMATIONS OF THE PLANE

Let S be the set of all points of an ordinary plane. In this section we consider some fundamental transformations of the set S onto itself.

3.2.1   *Definitions and Notation.*   Let $\overline{AB}$ be a directed line segment in the plane. By the *translation* $T(AB)$ we mean the transformation of S onto itself which carries each point P of the plane into the point P' of the plane such that $\overline{PP'}$ is equal and parallel to $\overline{AB}$. The directed segment $\overline{AB}$ is called the *vector* of the translation.

3.2.2   *Definitions and Notation.*   Let O be a fixed point of the plane and θ a given sensed angle. By the *rotation* $R(O, \theta)$ we mean the transformation of S onto itself which carries each point P of the plane into the point P' of the plane such that $OP' = OP$ and $\sphericalangle POP' = \theta$. Point O is called the *center* of the rotation, and θ is called the *angle* of the rotation.

3.2.3   *Definitions and Notation.*   Let l be a fixed line of the plane. By the *reflection* $R(l)$ *in line* l we mean the transformation of S onto itself which carries each point P of the plane into the point P' of the plane such that l is the perpendicular bisector of PP'. The line l is called the *axis* of the reflection.

3.2.4   *Definitions and Notation.*   Let O be a fixed point of the plane. By the *reflection* (or *half-turn*) $R(O)$ *in (about) point* O we mean the transformation of S onto itself which carries each point P of the plane into the point P' of the plane such that O is the midpoint of PP'. Point O is called the *center* of the reflection.

3.2.5   *Definitions and Notation.*   Let O be a fixed point of the plane and k a given nonzero real number. By the *homothety* (or *expansion*, or *dilatation*, or *stretch*) $H(O,k)$ we mean the transformation of S onto itself which carries each point P of the plane into the point P' of the plane such that $\overline{OP'} = k \overline{OP}$. The point O is called the *center* of the homothety, and k is called the *ratio* of the homothety.

There are certain products of the above transformations which also are of fundamental importance.

3.2.6   *Definitions and Notation.*   Let l be a fixed line of the plane and $\overline{AB}$ a given directed segment on l. By the *glide-reflection* $G(l, AB)$ we mean the product $R(l)\ T(AB)$. The line l is called the *axis* of the glide-reflection, and the directed segment $\overline{AB}$ on l is called the *vector* of the glide-reflection.

3.2.7   *Definitions and Notation.*   Let l be a fixed line of the plane and O a fixed point on l, and let k be a given nonzero real number. By the *stretch-reflection* $S(l,O,k)$ we mean the product $R(l)H(O,k)$. The line l is called the *axis* of the stretch-reflection, the point O is called the *center* of the stretch-reflection, and k is called the *ratio* of the stretch-reflection.

3.2.8   *Definitions and Notation.*   Let O be a fixed point of the plane, k a given nonzero real number, and θ a given sensed angle. By the *homology* (or *stretch-rotation,* or *spiral rotation*) $H(O,k,\theta)$ we mean the product $R(O,\theta)H(O,k)$. Point O is called the *center* of the homology, k the *ratio* of the homology, and θ the *angle* of the homology.

The following theorems are easy consequences of the above definitions.

3.2.9   *Theorem.*   *If* n *is an integer,   then* $R(O,(2n + 1)180°) = R(O) = H(O, -1)$.

3.2.10   *Theorem.*   *If* n *is an integer,   then* (1) $H(O,k,n360°) = H(O,k)$, (2) $H(O,k,(2n+1)\ 180°) = H(O,-k)$.

3.2.11   *Theorem.* $T(BC)T(AB) = T(AB)T(BC) = T(AC)$.

3.2.12   *Theorem.* $R(O,\theta_1)R(O,\theta_2) = R(O,\theta_2)R(O,\theta_1) = R(O,\theta_1 + \theta_2)$.

3.2.13   *Theorem.* $R(O,\theta)H(O,k) = H(O,k)R(O,\theta) = H(O,k,\theta)$.

3.2.14   *Theorem.*   *If* $\overline{AB}$ *is on* 1,   *then* $R(1)T(AB) = T(AB)R(1) = G(1,AB)$.

3.2.15   *Theorem.*   *If* O *is on* 1,   *then* $R(1)H(O,k) = H(O,k)R(1) = S(1,O,k)$.

3.2.16   *Theorem.*   (1) $[T(AB)]^{-1} = T(BA)$, (2) $[R(O,\theta)]^{-1} = R(O, -\theta)$, (3) $[R(1)]^{-1} = R(1)$, (4) $[R(O)]^{-1} = R(O)$, (5) $[H(O,k)]^{-1} = H(O,l/k)$, (6) $[G(1,AB)]^{-1} = G(1,BA)$, (7) $[H(O,k,\theta)]^{-1} = H(O,1/k, -\theta)$.

3.2.17   *Theorem.*   (1) $T(AA) = I$, (2) $R(O,n360°) = I$, *where* n *is any integer,* (3) $H(O, 1) = I$.

3.2.18   *Theorem.* $R(1)$ *and* $R(O)$ *are involutoric transformations.*

3.2.19   *Theorem.*   *In the unextended plane* (1) *a translation of non-zero vector has no invariant points,* (2) *a rotation of an angle which is not a multiple of* 360° *has only its center as an invariant point,* (3) *a reflection in a line has only the points of its axis as invariant points,* (4) *a reflection in a point has only its center as an invariant point,* (5) *a homothety of ratio different from* 1 *has only its center as an invariant point.*

PROBLEMS

3.2-1   Let O, P, M, N, referred to a rectangular cartesian coordinate system, be the points $(0,0), (1,1), (1,0), (2,0)$, respectively, and let l denote the x axis. Find the coordinates of the point P' obtained from the point P by the following transformations: (a) $T(OM)$, (b) $R(O,90°)$, (c) $R(l)$, (d) $R(M)$, (e) $R(O)$, (f) $H(O,2)$, (g) $H(N,-2)$, (h) $H(M,1/2)$, (i) $G(l,MN)$, (j) $S(l,O,2)$, (k) $H(O,2,90°)$, (l) $H(N,2,45°)$.

3.2-2   (a)   If $O_1 \neq O_2$, are the rotations $R(O_1,\theta_1)$ and $R(O_2,\theta_2)$ commutative?

(b)   Are $R(O)$ and $R(l)$ commutative?

(c)   Are $R(O_1 O_2)$ and $R(O_1,\theta)$ commutative?

(d)   Are $T(AB)$ and $R(l)$ commutative?

(e)   Are $T(AB)$ and $R(O)$ commutative?

3.2-3   If AB is carried into $A'B'$ by a rotation, locate the center of the rotation.

3.2-4   Let P map into P' under a glide-reflection. (a)   Show that PP' is bisected by the axis of the glide-reflection. (b) Show that the square of the glide-reflection is a translation of twice the vector of the glide-reflection.

3.2-5   Let $ABCD$ be a square with center O. Show that $R(B,90°)$ $R(C,90°) = R(O)$.

3.2-6   Let S be the square whose vertices are $A:(1,1)$, $B:(-1,1)$, $C:(-1,-1), D:(1,-1)$, and let O be the origin. Show that S is carried into itself under each of the transformations: $R(x$ axis$)$, $R(y$ axis$)$, $R(AC)$, $R(BD)$, $R(0,90°)$, $R(O)$, $R(O,270°)$, I.

3.2-7   Show that $R(O_2)R(O_1) = T(2O_1O_2)$.

3.2-8   (a)   Show that $T(AB)R(O)$ is a reflection in point O' such that $\overline{OO'}$ is equal and parallel to $(\overline{AB})/2$.

(b)   Show that $R(O)T(AB)$ is a reflection in point O' such that $\overline{O'O}$ is equal and parallel to $(\overline{AB})/2$.

(c)   Show that $T(OO')R(O) = R(M)$, where M is the midpoint of OO'.

3.3   APPLICATIONS OF HOMOTHETY

Before continuing our study of geometrical transformations, we pause to consider a few applications of the homothety transformation.

We first describe a linkage apparatus, known as a *pantograph*, which was invented about 1603 by the German astronomer Christolph Scheiner (*ca*. 1575 - 1650) for mechanically copying a figure on an enlarged or reduced scale. The instrument is made in a variety of forms and can be purchased in a good stationery store. One form is pictured in Fig. 3.3a, where the four equal rods are hinged by adjustable pivots at A, B, C, P, with $OA = AP$ and $PC = P'C = AB$. The instrument lies flat on the drawing paper and is fastened to the paper by a pointed pivot at O. Then if pencils are inserted at P and P', and P is made to trace a figure F, P' will trace the figure F' obtained from F by the homothety $H(O,\overline{OB}/\overline{OA})$. The reader can easily justify the working of the machine by showing that $APCB$ is a parallelogram, O, P, P' are collinear, and $\overline{OP'}/\overline{OP} = \overline{OB}/\overline{OA}$ = constant.

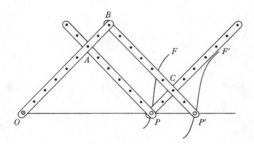

FIG. 3.3a

3.3.1   *Notation*. By the symbol $O(r)$ we mean the circle with center O and radius r.

3.3.2   *Definitions*. Let $A(a)$ and $B(b)$ be two nonconcentric circles and let I and E divide $\overline{AB}$ internally and externally in the ratio a/b. Then I and E are called the *internal* and *external centers of similitude* of the two circles (see Fig. 3.3b).

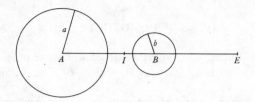

FIG. 3.3b

3.3.3 Theorem.

3.3.3   *Theorem.   Any two nonconcentric circles* A(a) *and* B(b) *with internal and external centers of similitude* I *and* E *are homothetic to each other under the homotheties* H(I, -b/a) *and* H(E, b/a).

Let P (see Fig. 3.3c) be any point on $A(a)$ not collinear with A and B. Let $P'BP''$ be the diameter of $B(b)$ parallel to AP, where $\overline{BP'}$ has the same direction as $\overline{AP}$. Let $P'P$ cut AB in E' and $P''P$ cut AB in I'. From similar triangles we find $\overline{E'P'}/\overline{E'P} = \overline{E'B}/\overline{E'A} = b/a$. Hence $E' = E$, the external center of similitude, and $B(b)$ is the image of $A(a)$ under the homothety $H(E,b/a)$. Similarly, $\overline{I'P''}/\overline{I'P} = \overline{I'B}/\overline{I'A} = -b/a$, and $I' = I$, the internal center of similitude. It follows that $B(b)$ is the image of $A(a)$ under the homothety $H(I, -b/a)$.

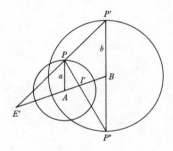

FIG. 3.3c

3.3.4 Theorem.

3.3.4   *Theorem.   The orthocenter* H, *the circumcenter* O, *and the centroid* G *of a triangle* $A_1 A_2 A_3$ *are collinear and* $\overline{HG} = 2\,\overline{GO}$.

Let M_1, M_2, M_3 (see Fig. 3.3d) be the midpoints of the sides $A_2 A_3, A_3 A_1, A_1 A_2$ of the triangle. Since $\overline{A_i G}/\overline{GM_i} = 2$ ($i = 1, 2, 3$), triangle $M_1 M_2 M_3$ is carried into triangle $A_1 A_2 A_3$ by the homothety $H(G, -2)$. Therefore O, which is the orthocenter of triangle $M_1 M_2 M_3$, maps into the orthocenter H of triangle $A_1 A_2 A_3$. It follows that H, G, O are collinear and $\overline{HG} = 2\,\overline{GO}$.

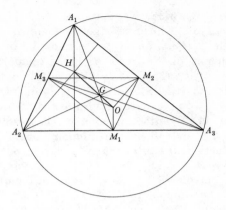

FIG. 3.3d

3.3.5 *Definition.* The line of collinearity of the orthocenter, circumcenter, and centroid of a triangle is called the *Euler line* of the triangle.

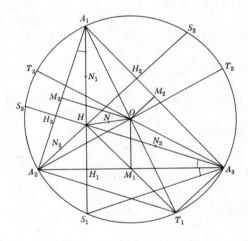

FIG. 3.3e

3.3.6 *Theorem.* In triangle $A_1 A_2 A_3$ let M_1, M_2, M_3 be the midpoints of the sides $A_2 A_3$, $A_3 A_1$, $A_1 A_2$, H_1, H_2, H_3 the feet of the altitudes on these sides, N_1, N_2, N_3 the midpoints of the segments $A_1 H$, $A_2 H$, $A_3 H$, where H is the orthocenter of the triangle. Then the nine points M_1, M_2, M_3, H_1, H_2, H_3, N_1, N_2, N_3 lie on a circle whose center N is the midpoint of the segment joining the orthocenter H to the circumcenter O of the triangle, and whose radius is half the circumradius of the triangle.

Referring to Fig. 3.3e, we see that $\angle A_2 A_3 H_3 = 90° - \angle A_2 = \angle A_2 A_1 S_1 = \angle A_2 A_3 S_1$. Therefore right triangle $HH_1 A_3$ is congruent to right triangle $S_1 H_1 A_3$, and H_1 is the midpoint of HS_1. Similarly, H_2 is the midpoint of HS_2 and H_3 is the midpoint of HS_3. Draw circumdiameter $A_1 T_1$. Then $T_1 A_2$ is parallel to $A_3 H_3$ (since each is perpendicular to $A_1 A_2$). Similarly, $T_1 A_3$ is parallel to $A_2 H_2$. Therefore $HA_3 T_1 A_2$ is a parallelogram and HT_1 and $A_2 A_3$ bisect each other. That is, M_1 is the midpoint of HT_1. Similarly, M_2 is the midpoint of HT_2 and M_3 is the midpoint of HT_3. It now follows that the homothety $H(H, 1/2)$ carries $A_1, A_2, A_3, S_1, S_2, S_3, T_1, T_2, T_3$ into $N_1, N_2, N_3, H_1, H_2, H_3, M_1, M_2, M_3$, whence these latter nine points lie on a circle of radius half that of the circumcircle and with center N at the midpoint of HO.

3.3.7 *Definition.* The circle of Theorem 3.3.6 is called the *nine-point circle* of triangle $A_1 A_2 A_3$.

It was O. Terquem who named this circle the *nine-point circle*, and this is the name commonly used in the English–speaking countries. Some French geometers refer to it as *Euler's circle*, and German geometers usually call it *Feuerbach's circle*.

3.3.8 *Definition.* Let I and E be the internal and external centers of similitude of two given nonconcentric circles $A(a)$, $B(b)$ having unequal radii. Then the circle on IE as diameter is called the *circle of similitude* of the two given circles.

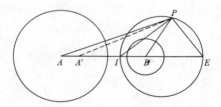

FIG. 3.3f

3.3.9 *Theorem.* *Let* P *be any point on the circle of similitude of two nonconcentric circles* A(a), B(b) *having unequal radii. Then* B(b) *is the image of* A(a) *under the homology* H(P, b/a, $\angle\overline{APB}$).

Let I and E be the internal and external centers of similitude of the two given circles. If P coincides with I or E the theorem follows from Theorem 3.3.3. If P is distinct from I and E (see Fig. 3.3f) then PI is perpendicular to PE and $(AB, IE) = -1$. Draw PA' so that PI bisects $\angle A'PB$ internally. Then PE is the external bisector of the same angle, and it follows that $(A'B, IE) = -1$.

Therefore $A' = A$ and $PB/PA = \overline{IB}/\overline{AI} = b/a$. The theorem now follows.

3.3.10   *Corollary.   The locus of a point* P *moving in a plane such that the ratio of its distance from point* A *to its distance from point* B *of the plane is a positive constant* $k \neq 1$ *is the circle on IE as diameter, where* I *and* E *divide the segment* $\overline{AB}$ *internally and externally in the ratio* k.

3.3.11   *Definition.*   The circle of Corollary 3.3.10 is called the *circle of Apollonius* of   points A and B for the ratio k (see Sec. 1.5).

PROBLEMS

3.3-1   In Fig. 3.3a show that O, P, P' are collinear and that $\overline{OP'}/\overline{OP} = \overline{OB}/\overline{OA}$.

3.3-2   Prove that if two circles have common external tangents, these tangents pass through the external center of similitude of the two circles, and if they have common internal tangents, these pass through the internal center of similitude of the two circles.

3.3-3   Let S be a center of similitude of two circles C_1 and C_2, and let one line through S cut C_1 in A and B and C_2 in A' and B', and a second line through S cut C_1 in C and D and C_2 in C' and D', where the primed points are the maps of the corresponding unprimed points under the homothety having center S and carrying circle C_1 into circle C_2. Show that: (a) $B'D'$ is parallel to BD,   (b) A', C', D, B are concyclic and A, C, D', B' are   concyclic,   (c) $(SA')(SB) = (SA)(SB') = (SC')(SD) = (SC)(SD')$,   (d)   the tangents to C_1 and C_2 at B and A' intersect on the radical axis of C_1 and C_2.

3.3-4   Prove that the circle of similitude of two nonconcentric circles with unequal radii is the locus of points from which the two circles subtend equal angles.

3.3-5   (a)   Show that the external centers of similitude of three circles with distinct centers taken in pairs are collinear.
(b)   Show that the external center of similitude of one pair of the circles and the internal centers of similitude of the other two pairs are collinear.

3.3-6   If a circle is tangent to each of two given circles, show that the line determined by the two points of tangency passes through a center of similitude of the two given circles.

3.3-7   If the distance between the centers of two circles $A(a)$ and $B(b)$ is c, locate the center of the circle of similitude of the two circles.

3.3-8   On the arc M_1H_1 of the nine-point circle, take the point X_1 one-third of the way from M_1 to H_1. Take similar points X_2 and X_3 on arcs M_2H_2 and M_3H_3. Show that triangle $X_1X_2X_3$ is equilateral.

3.4   ISOMETRIES AND SIMILARITIES

In this section we consider those point transformations of the unextended plane which preserve all lengths and those which preserve all shapes. These are known, respectively, as *isometries* and *similarities*. We commence with a formal definition of these concepts.

3.4.1   *Definitions.*   A point transformation of the unextended plane onto itself which carries each pair of points A, B into a pair A', B' such that $A'B' = k(AB)$, where k is a fixed positive number, is called a *similarity* (or an *equiform transformation*), and the particular case where $k = 1$ is called an *isometry* (or a *congruent transformation*). A similarity is said to be *direct* or *opposite* according as $\triangle ABC$ has or has not the same sense as $\triangle A'B'C'$. (A direct similarity is sometimes called a *similitude,* and an opposite similarity an *antisimilitude.* A direct isometry is sometimes called a *displacement,* and an opposite isometry a *reversal.*)

It is very interesting that isometries and similarities can be factored into products of certain of the fundamental point transformations considered in the previous section. We proceed to obtain some of these factorizations.

3.4.2   *Theorem.*   *There is a unique isometry that carries a triangle* ABC *into a congruent triangle* A'B'C'.

Superimposing the plane (by sliding, or turning it over and then sliding) upon its original position so that triangle ABC coincides with triangle $A'B'C'$ induces an isometry of the plane onto itself in which triangle ABC is carried into triangle $A'B'C'$. There is only the one isometry, for if P is any point in the plane there is a unique point P' in the plane such that $P'A' = PA$, $P'B' = PB$, $P'C' = PC$.

3.4.3   *Theorem.*   *Every isometry is the product of at most three reflections in lines.*

Let an isometry carry triangle ABC into triangle $A'B'C'$. We consider four cases. (1) If the two triangles coincide, the isometry (by Theorem 3.4.2) is the identity I, which may be considered as the product of the reflection $R(l)$ with itself, where l is any line in the plane. (2) If A coincides with A' and B with B', but C and C' are distinct, the isometry (by Theorem 3.4.2) is the reflection $R(l)$, where l is the line AB. (3) If A coincides with A', but B and B' and C and C' are distinct, the reflection $R(l)$, where l is the perpendicular bisector of BB', reduces this case to one of the two previous cases. (4) Finally, if A and A', B and B', C and C' are distinct, the reflection $R(l)$, where l is the perpendicular bisector of AA', reduces this case to one of the first three cases. In each case, the isometry is ultimately expressed as a product of no more than three reflections in lines.

3.4.4   *Theorem.   Every isometry containing an invariant point is the product of at most two reflections in lines.*

Let A be an invariant point of the isometry and let B and C be two points not collinear with A. Then triangle ABC is carried into triangle $A'B'C'$ where A' coincides with A. The desired result now follows from the first three cases in the proof of Theorem 3.4.3.

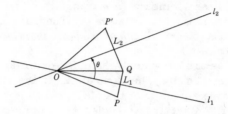

FIG. 3.4a

3.4.5   *Theorem.   Let l_1 and l_2 be any two lines of the plane intersecting in a point O, and let θ be the directed angle from l_1 to l_2, then $R(l_2)R(l_1) = R(O,2\theta)$. Conversely, a rotation $R(O,2\theta)$ can be factored into the product $R(l_2)R(l_1)$ of reflections in two lines l_1 and l_2 through O, where either line may be arbitrarily chosen through O and then the other such that the directed angle from l_1 to l_2 is equal to θ.*

The proof is apparent from Fig. 3.4a, since $OP' = OP$ and $\angle \overline{POP'} = \angle \overline{POQ} + \angle \overline{QOP'} = 2\angle \overline{L_1OQ} + 2\angle \overline{QOL_2} = 2\theta$.

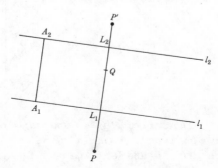

FIG. 3.4b

3.4.6   *Theorem.   Let* l_1 *and* l_2 *be any two parallel (or coincident) lines of the plane, and let* $\overline{A_1 A_2}$ *be the directed distance from line* l_1 *to line* l_2*; then* $R(l_2)R(l_1) = T(2A_1 A_2)$*. Conversely, a translation* $T(2A_1 A_2)$ *can be factored into the product* $R(l_2)R(l_1)$ *of reflections in two lines* l_1 *and* l_2 *perpendicular to* $A_1 A_2$*, where either line may be arbitrarily chosen perpendicular to* $A_1 A_2$ *and then the other such that the directed distance from* l_1 *to* l_2 *is equal to* $\overline{A_1 A_2}$.

The proof is apparent from Fig. 3.4b, since PP' is parallel to $A_1 A_2$ and $\overline{PP'} = \overline{PQ} + \overline{QP'} = 2\overline{L_1 Q} + 2\overline{QL_2} = 2A_1 A_2$.

3.4.7 *Theorem.   Any direct isometry is either a translation or a rotation.*

By Theorem 3.4.3, the isometry is a product of at most three reflections in lines. Since the isometry is direct, it must be a product of an *even* number of such reflections, and therefore of two such reflections. If the axes of the two reflections are parallel (or coincident), the isometry is a translation (by Theorem 3.4.6); otherwise the isometry is a rotation (by Theorem 3.4.5).

3.4.8   *Theorem.   There is a unique similarity that carries a triangle* ABC *into a similar triangle* A'B'C'.

If the triangles are congruent, the unique similarity is the unique isometry guaranteed by Theorem 3.4.2. If the triangles are not congruent, choose a point O of the plane. Now there is a homothety T_1 with center O carrying triangle ABC into a triangle $A''B''C''$ directly congruent to triangle $A'B'C'$, and (by Theorem 3.4.2) an isometry T_2 carrying triangle $A''B''C''$ into triangle $A'B'C'$. Therefore the similarity $T_2 T_1$ carries triangle ABC into triangle $A'B'C'$. But this is the only similarity, for if P is any point of the plane there is a unique point P' such that $P'A' = kPA$, $P'B' = kPB$, $P'C' = kPC$, where $k = A'B'/AB$.

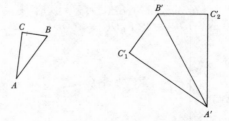

FIG. 3.4c

3.4.9   *Theorem.   There are exactly two similarities, one direct and one opposite, that carry a line segment* AB *into a line segment* A'B'.

Take C not on line AB and let C' be such that triangle $A'B'C'$ is similar to triangle *ABC*. There are exactly two possible positions for *C'*, marked C'_1 and C'_2 in Fig. 3.4c, and each position determines (by Theorem 3.4.8) a unique similarity carrying triangle *ABC* into triangle *A'B'C'*. Since triangles $A'B'C'_1$ and $A'B'C'_2$ can be carried into one another by a reflection in line *A'B'*, it follows that one of the similarities is direct and the other opposite.

3.4.10   *Theorem.*   *If a similarity carries each line of the plane into a parallel line of the plane, then the similarity is either a translation or a homothety.*

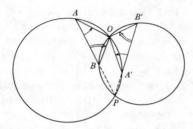

FIG. 3.4d$_1$

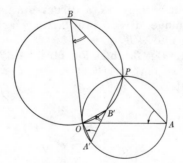

FIG. 3.4d$_2$

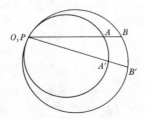

FIG. 3.4d$_3$

Consider a triangle ABC; it is carried into a triangle $A'B'C'$ whose sides are parallel to the corresponding sides of triangle ABC. It follows that the two triangles are coaxial (on the line at infinity), and therefore (by Desargues' two-triangle theorem) also copolar at a point P. If P is an ideal point, the similarity is the translation $T(AA')$; if P is an ordinary point, the similarity is the homothety $H(P, \overline{A'B'}/\overline{AB})$.

3.4.11   Theorem.   *Any direct similarity is either a translation or a homology.*

In view of Theorem 3.4.10, this is certainly the case if the similarity carries each line into a parallel line.

Suppose that the similarity does not carry each line into a parallel line. Then there are two nonparallel segments AB and $A'B'$ such that AB is carried into $A'B'$. Let lines $AB, A'B'$ intersect in P (see Figs. $3.4d_1, d_2, d_3$), and suppose that P is not an endpoint of either of the two segments. Draw circles $AA'P$ and $BB'P$ and let O be their other point of intersection, which is taken at P if the circles happen to be tangent to one another there. Then $\measuredangle \overline{BAO} = \measuredangle \overline{B'A'O}, \measuredangle \overline{ABO} = \measuredangle \overline{A'B'O}$, and triangle (or collinear triad) ABO is directly similar to triangle (or collinear triad) $A'B'O$. It follows that AB is carried into $A'B'$ under the homology $H(O, A'B'/AB, \measuredangle \overline{AOA'})$. Since a homology is a direct similarity, the above homology is the unique direct similarity guaranteed by Theorem 3.4.9 carrying AB into $A'B'$.

If, for example, $P = B$, then for circle $BB'P$ we take the circle through B' and tangent to AB at B (see Fig. 3.4e). The proof is then exactly as before.

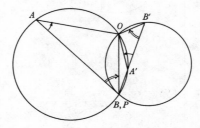

FIG. 3.4e

3.4.12   Theorem.   *If the line segments joining corresponding points of two given directly similar figures be divided proportionately, the locus of the dividing points is a figure directly similar to the given figures.*

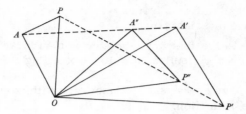

FIG. 3.4f

By Theorem 3.4.11, the two given figures are related by a translation or a homology. The case of a translation presents no
difficulty; the locus of the dividing points is clearly a figure
directly congruent to each of the two given figures. Suppose, then,
that the two given figures are related by a homology $H(O,k,\theta)$.
Let (see Fig. 3.4f) A,A' be a fixed and P,P' a variable pair of
corresponding points in the two given figures. Then $OP'/OP =
OA'/OA = k$ and $\measuredangle POP' = \measuredangle AOA' = \theta$. Let P'' and A'' be taken on
AA' and PP' such that $\overline{PP''}/\overline{P'P} = \overline{AA''}/\overline{A''A'}$. Since triangles POP'
and AOA' are directly similar, it follows that triangles POP'' and
AOA'' are also directly similar, and $OP''/OP = OA''/OA = k'$, say,
and $\measuredangle POP'' = \measuredangle AOA'' = \theta$, say. It follows that the locus of P'' is the
image of the locus of P under the homology $H(O,k',\theta')$. That is, the
locus of P'' is a figure directly similar to the two given figures.

Further analysis can be given to yield the following two theorems
(which we here accept without proof).

3.4.13   *Theorem.   Any opposite isometry is either a reflection in a
line or a glide-reflection.*

3.4.14   *Theorem.   Any opposite similarity is either a glide-reflection
or a stretch–reflection.*

PROBLEMS

3.4-1   Show that there are exactly two isometries, one direct
and one opposite, that carry a line segment AB into a congruent line segment $A'B'$.

3.4-2   Prove that a product of three reflections in lines is either
a reflection in a line or a glide-reflection.

3.4-3   (a)   Show that the product of two rotations is a rotation
or a translation.

(b)   Show that a direct isometry which is not a translation has exactly one invariant point.

3.4-4   (a)   Prove that any isometry with an invariant point is a rotation or a reflection in a line according as it is direct or opposite.

(b)   Prove that every opposite isometry with no invariant point is a glide-reflection.

(c)   Prove that if an isometry has more than one invariant point, it must be either the identity or a reflection in a line.

3.4-5   (a)   Prove that any direct similarity which is not a translation has an invariant point.

(b)   Prove that any opposite similarity which is not a glide-reflection has an invariant point.

3.4-6   (a)   Show that if T is an opposite isometry, then T^2 is the identity or a translation.

(b)   Show that if T is an opposite similarity, then T^2 is a translation or a homothety.

3.4-7   (a)   Show that $R(l)T(AB)$ is a glide-reflection whose axis is a line m parallel to l at a distance equal to one-half the projection of $\overline{AB}$ on a line perpendicular to l, and whose vector is the projection of $\overline{AB}$ on l.

(b)   Show that $T(AB)R(l)$ is a glide-reflection whose axis is a line m parallel to l at a distance equal to one-half the projection of $\overline{BA}$ on a line perpendicular to l, and whose vector is the projection of $\overline{AB}$ on l.

3.4-8   Prove Hjelmslev's Theorem: When all the points P on one line are related by an isometry to all the points P' on another line, the midpoints of the segments PP' are distinct and collinear, or else they all coincide.

3.4-9   Show that every opposite isometry is the product of a reflection in a line and a reflection in a point.

3.4-10   Show that $T(BA)R(O,\theta)T(AB) = R(O',\theta)$, where $\overline{O'O}$ is equal and parallel to $\overline{AB}$.

3.4-11   Let O, O' be two points on line l. Show that $G(l,2OO') = R(O')R(m)$, where m is the line through O perpendicular to l.

3.4-12   If two maps of the same country on different scales are drawn on tracing paper and then superposed, show that there is just one place that is represented by the same spot on both maps.

3.4-13   (a)   On the sides BC and CA of a triangle ABC, construct externally any two directly similar triangles, CBA_1 and ACB_1. Show that the midpoints of the three segments BC, A_1B_1, CA form a triangle directly similar to the two given triangles.

(b)   On BC externally and on CA internally, construct any two directly similar triangles CBA_1 and CAB_1. Show that the midpoints of AB and A_1B_1 form with C a triangle directly similar to the two given triangles.

3.5   INVERSION

In this section we briefly consider the inversion transformation, which is perhaps the most useful transformation we have for simplifying plane figures.

Inversely related points were known to François Viète in the sixteenth century. Robert Simson, in his 1749 restoration of Apollonius' lost work *Plane Loci*, included (on the basis of commentary made by Pappus) one of the basic theorems of the theory of inversion, namely, that the inverse of a straight line or a circle is a straight line or a circle. Simon A. J. L'Huilier (1750-1840) in his   *Eléments d'analyse géométrique et d'analyse algébrique appliquées à la recherche des lieux géométriques*   (Paris and Geneva, 1808) gave special cases of this theorem.

But inversion as a simplifying transformation for the study of figures is a product of more recent times, and was independently exploited by a number of writers. Bützberger has pointed out that Jacob Steiner disclosed, in an unpublished manuscript, a knowledge of the inversion transformation as early as 1824. It was refound in the following year by the Belgian astronomer and statistician Adolphe Quetelet. It was then found independently by L. I. Magnus, in a more general form, in 1831, by J. Bellavitis in 1836, then by J. W. Stubbs and J. R. Ingram, two Fellows of Trinity College, Dublin, in 1842 and 1843, and by Sir William Thomson (Lord Kelvin) in 1845. Thomson used inversion to give geometrical proofs of some difficult propositions in the mathematical theory of elasticity. In 1847 Liouville called inversion the *transformation by reciprocal radii*. Because of a property to be established shortly, inversion has also been called *reflection in a circle*.

3.5.1   *Definitions and Notation.*   If point P is not the center O of circle $O(r)$, the *inverse* of P in, or with respect to, circle $O(r)$ is the point P' lying on the line OP such that $(\overline{OP})(\overline{OP'}) = r^2$. Circle $O(r)$

is called the *circle of inversion*, point O the *center of inversion*, r the *radius of inversion*, and r^2 the *power of inversion*. We denote the inversion with center O and power $k > 0$ by the symbol $I(O,k)$.

From the above definition it follows that to each point P of the plane, other than O, there corresponds a unique inverse point P', and that if P' is the inverse of P, then P is the inverse of P'. Since there is no point corresponding, under the inversion, to the center O of inversion, we do not have a transformation of the set S of all points of the plane onto itself. In order to make inversion a transformation, as defined in Definition 3.1.2, we may do either of two things. We may let S' denote the set of all points of the plane except for the single point O, and then inversion will be a transformation of the "punctured plane" S' onto itself. Or we may add to the set S of all points in the plane a single ideal "point at infinity" to serve as the correspondent under the inversion of the center O of inversion, and then the inversion will be a transformation of this augmented set S'' onto itself. It turns out that the second approach is the more convenient one, and we accordingly adopt the following convention.

3.5.2   *Convention and Definitions.*   When working with inversion, we add to the set S of all points of the plane a single ideal point at infinity, to be considered as lying on every line of the plane, and this ideal point Z shall be the image under the inversion of the center O of inversion, and the center O of inversion shall be the image under the inversion of this ideal point Z. The plane, augmented in this way, will be referred to as the *inversive plane*.

Of course, Convention 3.5.2 is at variance with the earlier Convention 2.2.1. But conventions are made only for convenience, and no trouble will arise if one states clearly which, if either, convention is being employed. For some investigations it is convenient to work in the ordinary plane, for others, in the extended plane, and for still others, in the inversive plane. It is to be understood that throughout the present section we shall be working in the inversive plane. The following theorem is apparent.

3.5.3   *Theorem.   Inversion is an involutoric transformation of the inversive plane onto itself which maps the interior of the circle of inversion onto the exterior of the circle of inversion and each point on the circle of inversion onto itself.*

One naturally wonders if there are any other self–inverse loci besides the circle of inversion. The next theorem deals with this matter—but first we make a convenient definition and convention.

3.5.4 *Definition and Convention.* We shall call a circle or a straight line a *"circle"* (with quotation marks), and we shall adopt the convention that two straight lines are *tangent* if and only if they either coincide or are parallel. With this convention, it is perfectly clear in all cases what is meant by two "circles" being tangent to one another.

3.5.5 *Theorem. A "circle" orthogonal to the circle of inversion inverts into itself.*

This is obvious if the "circle" is a straight line, and the proof of Theorem 2.6.3 takes care of the case where the "circle" is a circle. Note that the "circle" inverts into itself as a whole and not point by point.

The following theorem suggests an easy way to construct the inverse of any given point distinct from the center of inversion.

3.5.6 *Theorem. A point* D *outside the circle of inversion, and the point* C *where the chord of contact of the tangents from* D *to the circle of inversion cuts the diametral line* OD, *are inverse points.*

For (see Fig. 3.5a), $(\overline{OD})\,(\overline{OC}) = (OT)^2 = r^2$.

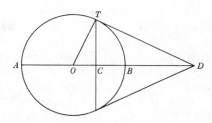

FIG. 3.5a

The following four theorems relate the concept of inverse points with some earlier concepts.

3.5.7 *Theorem. If* C, D *are inverse points with respect to circle* O(r), *then* (AB,CD) = - 1, *where* AB *is the diameter of* O(r) *through* C *and* D; *conversely, if* (AB,CD) = - 1, *where* AB *is a diameter of circle* O(r), *then* C *and* D *are inverse points with respect to circle* O(r).

For (see Fig. 3.5a), $(\overline{OC})\,(\overline{OD}) = r^2 = (OB)^2$ if and only if $(AB,CD) = -1$ (by Theorem 2.5.5).

3.5.8 *Theorem. If* C, D *are inverse points with respect to circle* O(r), *then any circle through* C *and* D *cuts circle* O(r) *orthogonally; conversely, if a diameter of circle* O(r) *cuts a circle orthogonal to* O(r) *in* C *and* D, *then* C *and* D *are inverse points with respect to* O(r).

This, in view of Theorem 3.5.7, is merely an alternative statement of Theorem 2.6.3.

3.5.9   *Theorem.   If two intersecting circles are each orthogonal to a third circle, then the points of intersection of the two circles are inverse points with respect to the third circle.*

Let the two circles intersect in points C and D and let O be the center of the third circle. Draw OC to cut the two given circles again in D' and D''. Then D' and D'' are each (by Theorem 3.5.8) the inverse of C with respect to the third circle. It follows that $D' = D'' = D$, and C and D are inverse points with respect to the third circle.

It is Theorem 3.5.9 that has led some geometers to refer to inversion as *reflection in a circle.* For if two intersecting circles are each orthogonal to a straight line, then the points of intersection of the two circles are reflections of each other in the line. Therefore, using the terminology "reflection in a circle" for "inversion with respect to a circle," and recalling Convention 3.5.2, we may subsume both the above fact and Theorem 3.5.9 in the single statement: *If two intersecting "circles" are each orthogonal to a third "circle," then the points of intersection of the two "circles" are reflections of each other in the third "circle."* Of course the same end can be achieved by using the terminology "inversion in a line" for "reflection in a line," and some geometers do just this.

3.5.10   *Theorem.* $I(O,k_2)I(O,k_1) = H(O,k_2/k_1)$.

Let P be any point and let $I(O,k_1)$ carry P into P' and let $I(O,k_2)$ carry P' into P''. Then, if $P \neq 0$, we have O, P, P', P'' collinear and $(\overline{OP})\,(\overline{OP'}) = k_1$, $(\overline{OP'})\,(\overline{OP''}) = k_2$, whence O, P, P'' are collinear and $\overline{OP''}/\overline{OP} = k_2/k_1$. If $P = O$, then $P' = Z$, $P'' = O$. The theorem now follows.

3.6   PROPERTIES OF INVERSION

When a point P traces a given curve C, the inverse point P' traces a curve C' called the *inverse* of the given curve. The next four theorems investigate the nature of the inverses of straight lines and circles. The first of the theorems has already been established as part of Theorem 3.5.5.

3.6.1   *Theorem.   The inverse of a straight line* l *passing through the center* O *of inversion is the line* l *itself.*

3.6.2   *Theorem.   The inverse of a straight line* l *not passing through the center* O *of inversion ᵼs a circle* C *passing through* O *and having its diameter through* O *perpendicular to* 1.

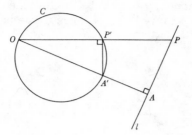

FIG. 3.6a

Let point A (see Fig. 3.6a) be the foot of the perpendicular dropped from O on l. Let P be any other ordinary point on l and let A', P' be the inverses of A, P. Then $(\overline{OA})(\overline{OA'}) = (\overline{OP})(\overline{OP'})$, whence $OP'/OA' = OA/OP$ and triangles $OP'A'$, OAP are similar. Therefore $\angle OP'A' = \angle OAP = 90°$. It follows that P' lies on the circle C having OA' as diameter. Conversely, if P' is any point on circle C other than O or A', let OP' cut line l in P. Then, by the above, P' must be the inverse of P. Note that point O on circle C corresponds to the point Z at infinity on l.

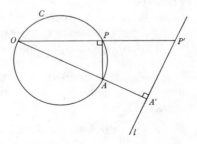

FIG. 3.6b

3.6.3   Theorem.   *The inverse of a circle* C *passing through the center* O *of inversion is a straight line* 1 *not passing through* O *and perpendicular to the diameter of* C *through* O.

Let point A (see Fig. 3.6b) be the point on C diametrically opposite O, and let P be any point on circle C other than O and A. Let A', P' be the inverses of A, P. Then $(\overline{OA})(\overline{OA'}) = (\overline{OP})(\overline{OP'})$, whence $OP'/OA' = OA/OP$ and triangles $OP'A'$, OAP are similar.

Therefore $\angle OA'P' = \angle OPA = 90°$. It follows that P' lies on the line l through A' and perpendicular to OA. Conversely, if P' is any ordinary point on line l other than A', let OP' cut the circle C in P. Then, by the above, P' must be the inverse of P. Note that the point Z at infinity on line l corresponds to the point O on circle C.

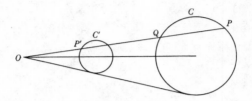

FIG. 3.6c

3.6.4 *Theorem. The inverse of a circle C not passing through the center O of inversion is a circle C' not passing through O and homothetic to circle C with O as center of homothety.*

Let P (see Fig. 3.6c) be any point on circle C. Let P' be the inverse of P and let OP cut circle C again in Q, Q coinciding with P if OP is tangent to circle C. Let r^2 be the power of inversion and let k be the power of point O with respect to circle C. Then $(\overline{OP})(\overline{OP'}) = r^2$ and $(\overline{OP})(\overline{OQ}) = k$, whence $\overline{OP'}/\overline{OQ} = r^2/k$, a constant. It follows that P' describes the map of the locus of Q under the homothety $H(O, r^2/k)$. That is, P' describes a circle C' homothetic to circle C and having O as center of homothety. Since circle C does not pass through O, circle C' also does not pass through O.

3.6.5 *Definition.* A point transformation of the inversive plane onto itself that carries "circles" into "circles" is called a *circular*, or *Möbius*, *transformation*.

Combining Theorems 3.6.1 through 3.6.4 we have:

3.6.6 *Theorem. Inversion is a circular transformation.*

We now establish a very useful theorem concerning directed angles between two "circles." We need the following lemma, whose easy proof will be left to the reader.

3.6.7 *Lemma. Let C' (see Figs. 3.6d$_1$ and 3.6d$_2$) be the inverse of "circle" C, and let P, P' be a pair of (perhaps coincident) corresponding points, under an inversion of center O, on C and C' respectively. Then the tangents (see Definition 3.5.4) to C and C' at P and P' are reflections of one another in the perpendicular to OP through the midpoint of PP'.*

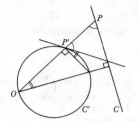

FIG. 3.6d₁

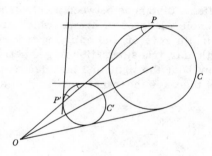

FIG. 3.6d₂

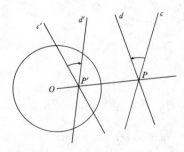

FIG. 3.6e

3.6.8   *Theorem.   A directed angle of intersection of two "circles" is
unaltered in magnitude but reversed in sense by an inversion.*

Let C and D be two "circles" intersecting in a point P, their
inverses C' and D' intersecting in the inverse P' of P. Let c and d
(see Fig. 3.6e) be the tangents to C and D at P, and let c' and d' be
the tangents to C' and D' at P'. Since, by Lemma 3.6.7, c and c',

as well as d and d', are reflections of one another in the perpendicular to OP at the midpoint of PP', it follows that the directed angle from c to d is equal but opposite to the directed angle from c' to d'.

In particular we have:

3.6.9   *Corollary.*   (1) *If two "circles" are tangent, their inverses are tangent. (2) If two "circles" are orthogonal, their inverses are orthogonal.*

There are other things, besides the magnitudes of angles between "circles," which remain invariant under an inversion transformation. Theorem 3.6.10 gives a useful invariant of this sort. Theorem 3.6.11 is an important metrical theorem which shows how inversion affects distances between points. Theorem 3.6.12 is a sample of a whole class of theorems which are valuable when using inversion in its role of a simplifying transformation. When employing a particular transformation in geometry it is of course important to know both the principal invariants of the transformation and some of the ways the transformation can simplify figures.

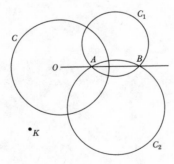

FIG. 3.6f

3.6.10   *Theorem.*   (1) *If a circle and two inverse points be inverted with respect to a center not on the circle, we obtain a circle and two inverse points. (2) If a circle and two inverse points be inverted with respect to a center on the circle, we obtain a straight line and two points which are reflections of one another in the straight line.*

Let points A and B (see Fig. 3.6f) be inverse points with respect to a circle C and let K be any point. Draw circles C_1, C_2 through A and B but not through K. C_1, C_2 are orthogonal to C (by Theorem 3.5.8). Invert the figure with respect to center K.

(1)   If K is not on C, we obtain circles C', C'_1, C'_2 and points A', B'. By Corollary 3.6.9, C'_1 and C'_2 are orthogonal to C', whence (by

Theorem 3.5.9) A' and B' are inverse with respect to circle C'.

(2)   If K is on C, we obtain a straight line C', circles C'_1, C'_2, and points A', B'. By Corollary 3.6.9, C'_1 and C'_2 are orthogonal to C'. It follows that A', B' are reflections of one another in line C'.

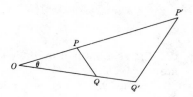

FIG. 3.6g

3.6.11   *Theorem.   If* P, P' *and* Q, Q' *are pairs of inverse points with respect to circle* O(r), *then* $P'Q' = (PQ)r^2/(OP)(OQ)$.

Suppose (see Fig. 3.6g) that O, P, Q are not collinear. Since $(OP)(OP') = (OQ)(OQ')$, triangle OPQ is similar to triangle $OQ'P'$, whence $P'Q'/PQ = OQ'/OP = (OQ')(OQ)/(OP)(OQ) = r^2/(OP)(OQ)$.

The case where O, P, Q are collinear follows from the above case by letting angle θ (see Fig. 3.6g) approach zero. Or we may give a separate proof as follows (see Fig. 3.6h):

$$(\overline{OP})(\overline{OP'}) = (\overline{OQ})(\overline{OQ'}),$$

$$(\overline{OQ} + \overline{QP})\,\overline{OP'} = \overline{OQ}\,(\overline{OP'} + \overline{P'Q'}),$$

$$(\overline{QP})(\overline{OP'}) = (\overline{OQ})(\overline{P'Q'}),$$

$$\overline{P'Q'} = (\overline{QP})(\overline{OP'})/\overline{OQ} = (\overline{QP})(\overline{OP'})(\overline{OP})/(\overline{OP})(\overline{OQ}) = (\overline{QP})r^2/(\overline{OP})(\overline{OQ}).$$

FIG. 3.6h

3.6.12   *Theorem.   Two nonintersecting circles can always be inverted into a pair of concentric circles.*

Let C_1 and C_2 be a pair of nonintersecting circles, and let l be their radical axis. Using two points on l as centers, draw two circles D_1 and D_2 each orthogonal to both C_1 and C_2. Then (by Theorem 2.6.14(1)) D_1 and D_2 intersect in two points P_1 and P_2. Choose either of these two points, say P_1, as a center of inversion and invert the entire figure. C_1 and C_2 (by Theorem 3.6.4) become circles C'_1 and C'_2. D_1 and D_2 (by Theorem 3.6.3) become straight lines D'_1 and D'_2, each of which (by Corollary 3.6.9(2)) cuts circles C'_1 and C'_2 orthogonally. This means that C'_1 and C'_2 are concentric.

PROBLEMS

3.6-1 (a) Draw the figure obtained by inverting a square with respect to its center.

(b) Draw the figure obtained by inverting a square with respect to one of its vertices.

3.6-2 (a) What is the inverse of a system of concurrent lines with respect to a point distinct from the point of concurrence?

(b) What is the inverse of a system of parallel lines?

3.6-3 Prove that a coaxial system of circles inverts into a coaxial system of circles or into a set of concurrent or parallel lines.

3.6-4 (a) Let O be a point on a circle of center C, and let the inverse of this circle with respect to O as center of inversion intersect OC in B. If C' is the inverse of C, show that $OB = BC'$.

(b) Show that the inverse C' of the center C of a given circle K is the inverse of the center O of inversion in the circle K' which is the inverse of the given circle K.

(c) Calling reflection in a line inversion in the line, state the facts of parts (a) and (b) as a single theorem.

(d) Prove that if two circles are orthogonal, the inverse of the center of either with respect to the other is the midpoint of their common chord.

3.6-5 (a) If $A(a)$ and $B(b)$ are two orthogonal circles, show that $I(B,b^2)I(A,a^2) = I(A,a^2)I(B,b^2)$.

(b) If K_1,K_2 are two orthogonal circles, A, A' inverse points in K_1, B and B' the inverses of A and A' in K_2, show that B, B' are inverse points in K_1.

3.6-6 If A, B, C, D are four concyclic points in the order A, C, B, D, and if p, q, r are the lengths of the perpendiculars from D to the lines AB, BC, CA, respectively, show that

$$AB/p = BC/q + CA/r.$$

3.6-7 Prove that the product of three inversions in three circles of a coaxial system is an inversion in a circle of that system.

3.6-8 We call the product $R(O)I(O,r^2)$ an *antinversion* in circle $O(r)$.

(a) Show that an antinversion is a circular transformation.

(b) Show that a circle through a pair of antinverse points for a circle K cuts K diametrically.

3.6-9 (a) Show that two circles can be inverted into themselves from any point on their radical axis and outside both circles.

(b) When can three circles be inverted into themselves?

3.6-10 Show that a nonintersecting coaxial system of circles can be inverted into a system of concentric circles.

3.6-11 Show that any three nonintersecting circles can be inverted into three circles whose centers are collinear.

3.6-12 Show that any three points can, in general, be inverted into the vertices of a triangle similar to a given triangle.

3.6-13 Show that any three noncollinear points can be inverted into the vertices of an equilateral triangle of given size.

3.6-14 Circle C_1 inverts into circle C_2 with respect to circle C. Show that C_1 and C_2 invert into equal circles with respect to any point on circle C.

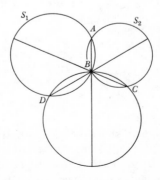

FIG. 3.7a$_1$

3.7   APPLICATION OF INVERSION

We give a few illustrations of inversion as a simplifying transformation. We first emphasize the *transform-solve-invert* procedure,
described in the introduction to this chapter, by an informal discussion of the problem (see Fig. 3.7a_1):

Let two circles S_1 *and* S_2 *intersect in* A *and* B, *and let the diameters of*
S_1 *and* S_2 *through* B *cut* S_2 *and* S_1 *in* C *and* D. *Show that line* AB *passes*
through the center of circle BCD.

The figure of the problem involves three lines and three circles,
all passing through a common point B. This suggests that we
transform the figure into a simpler one by an inversion having
center B, for under such an inversion the three lines will (by
Theorem 3.6.1) map into themselves, and the three circles will
(by Theorem 3.6.3) map into three lines. For convenience, we
sketch the appearance of the simplified figure, not upon the first
figure, as it would naturally appear, but separated from the first
figure (see Fig. 3.7a_2). Note that circles BCD, $S_1 = ABD$, $S_2 = ABC$
have become straight lines $D'C'$, $A'D'$, $A'C'$, respectively, and the
straight lines AB, CB, DB have become the straight lines $A'B$,
$C'B$, $D'B$, respectively. Since line BC, being a diametral line of
circle S_1, cuts S_1 orthogonally, we have (by Corollary 3.6.9 (2))
that BC' is perpendicular to $S'_1 = A'D'$. Similarly, we have that BD'
is perpendicular to $S'_2 = A'C'$.

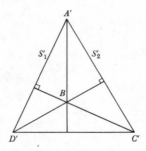

FIG. 3.7a_2

Now it is our desire to show that AB is a diametral line of circle
BCD, or, in other words, to show that AB is orthogonal to circle
BCD. We therefore attempt to *solve* , in the simplified figure, the
allied problem: *Show that* A'B *is perpendicular to* D'C'. But this is easily
accomplished, for, since BC' and BD' are perpendicular to $A'D'$

and $A'C'$, respectively, B is the orthocenter of triangle $A'D'C'$, and $A'B$ must be perpendicular to $D'C'$.

Since $A'B$ is perpendicular to $D'C'$, if we *invert* the transformation that carried the first figure into the simplified one, we discover that AB is orthogonal to circle BCD, and our original problem is now solved.

The three-part procedure, *transform-solve-invert*, has carried us through. Our problem has turned out to be nothing but the inverse, with respect to the orthocenter as center of inversion, of the fact that the three altitudes of a triangle are concurrent, and the relation of the problem might well have been first discovered in just this way.

The five applications of inversion which now follow will be sketched only briefly, and the reader is invited to supply any missing details.

PTOLEMY'S THEOREM

The following proposition was brilliantly employed by Claudius Ptolemy (ca. 85–ca. 165) for the development of a table of chords in the first book of his *Almagest*, the great definitive Greek work on astronomy. In all probability the proposition was known before Ptolemy's time, but his proof of it is the first that has come down to us. It is interesting that a very simple demonstration of the proposition—indeed, of an extension of the proposition—can be given by means of the inversion transformation.

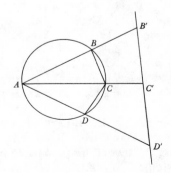

FIG. 3.7b

3.7.1   *Ptolemy's Theorem.   In a cyclic convex quadrilateral the product of the diagonals is equal to the sum of the products of the two pairs of
opposite sides.*

Referring to Fig. 3.7b, subject the quadrilateral and its circumcircle to the inversion $I(A,1)$. The vertices B, C, D map into
points B', C', D' lying on a straight line. It follows that $B'C' + C'D' =
B'D'$, whence (by Theorem 3.6-11)

$$BC/(AB \cdot AC) + CD/(AC \cdot AD) = BD/(AB \cdot AD)$$

or

$$BC \cdot AD + CD \cdot AB = BD \cdot AC.$$

If quadrilateral $ABCD$ is not cyclic, then B', C', D' will lie on a
circle and $B'C' + C'D' > B'D'$. Using this fact the reader can easily
supply a proof, fashioned after the above, for the following:

3.7.2   *Extension of Ptolemy's Theorem.   In a convex quadrilateral*
ABCD,

$$BC \cdot AD + CD \cdot AB \geqq BD \cdot AC,$$

with equality if and only if the quadrilateral is cyclic.

PAPPUS' ANCIENT THEOREM

In Book IV of Pappus' *Collection* appears the following beautiful
proposition, referred to by Pappus as being already ancient in his
time.   The proof of the proposition by inversion is singularly
attractive.

3.7.3   *Pappus' Ancient Theorem.   Let X, Y, Z be three collinear
points with Y between X and Z, and let C, C_1, K_0 denote semicircles, all
lying on the same side of XZ, on XZ, XY, YZ as diameters.   Let K_1, K_2,
K_3, $\cdots$ denote circles touching C and C_1, with K_1 also touching K_0, K_2 also
touching K_1, K_3 also touching K_2, and so on.   Denote the radius of K_n by r_n,
and the distance of the center of K_n from XZ by h_n.   Then $h_n = 2nr_n$.*

Subject the figure to the inversion $I(X, t_n{}^2)$, where t_n is the
tangent length from X to circle K_n. Then (see Fig. 3.7c) K_n inverts
into itself, C and C_1 invert into a pair of parallel lines tangent to
K_n and perpendicular to XZ. K_0, K_1, K_2, $\cdots$, K_{n-1} invert into a
semicircle and circles, all of the same radius, tangent to the two
parallel lines and such that K'_1 touches K'_0, K'_2 touches K'_1, $\cdots$,
K'_{n-1} touches K'_{n-2} and also K_n. It is now clear that $h_n = 2nr_n$.

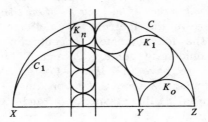

FIG. 3.7c

FEUERBACH'S THEOREM

Geometers universally regard the so-called Feuerbach's Theorem as undoubtedly one of the most beautiful theorems in the modern geometry of the triangle. The theorem was first stated and proved by Karl Wilhelm Feuerbach (1800 - 1834) in a work of his published in 1822; his proof was of a computational nature and employed trigonometry. A surprising number of proofs of the theorem have been given since, but probably none is as neat as the following proof employing the inversion transformation. We first state two definitions.

3.7.4   *Definition.*   A circle tangent to one side of a triangle and to the other two sides produced is called an *excircle* of the triangle. (There are four circles touching all three side lines of a triangle — the incircle and three excircles.)

3.7.5   *Definition.*   Two lines are said to be *antiparallel* relative to two transversals if the four lines form a cyclic quadrilateral having the two lines along one pair of opposite sides.

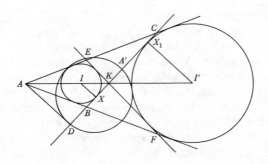

FIG. 3.7d

3.7.6 *Feuerbach's Theorem. The nine-point circle of a triangle is tangent to the incircle and to each of the excircles of the triangle.*

Figure 3.7d shows the incircle (I) and one excircle (I') of a triangle ABC. The four common tangents to these two circles determine the homothetic centers A and K lying on the line of centers II', and we have $(AK, II') = -1$. If D, X, X_1 are the feet of the perpendiculars from A, I, I' on line BC, we then have $(DK, XX_1) = -1$. Now the line segments BC and XX_1 have a common midpoint A', and

$$(A'K) (A'D) = (A'X)^2 = (A'X_1)^2. \qquad (3.1)$$

Subject the figure to the inversion $I(A', \overline{A'X^2})$. The circles (I) and (I') invert into themselves. Since the nine-point circle passes through A' and D, it follows that this circle inverts into a straight line through $\bar{K}$, the inverse of D by Eq. (3.1). Also, the angle which this line makes with BC is equal but opposite to the angle which the tangent to the nine-point circle at D makes with BC, or is therefore equal in both magnitude and sign to the angle which the tangent to the nine-point circle at A' makes with BC. But it is easily shown that this latter tangent is parallel to the opposite side of the orthic triangle, and therefore antiparallel to BC relative to AB and AC. But EF is antiparallel to BC relative to AB and AC. It follows that line EF is the inverse of the nine-point circle. Since this line is tangent to both (I) and (I'), we have that the nine-point circle is tangent to both (I) and (I'). That the nine-point circle is tangent to each of the other excircles can be shown in a like manner.

STEINER'S PORISM

Consider a circle C_1 lying entirely within another circle C_2, and a sequence of circles, $K_1, K_2, \cdots$, each having external contact with C_1 and internal contact with C_2, and such that K_2 touches K_1, K_3 touches K_2, and so on. A number of interesting questions suggest themselves in connection with such a figure. For example, can it ever be that the sequence $K_1, K_2, \cdots$ is finite, in the sense that finally a circle K_n of the sequence is reached which touches both K_{n-1} and K_1? Do the points of contact of the circles $K_1, K_2, \cdots$ lie on a circle? Do their centers lie on a circle? Etc. The figure was a dear one to Jacob Steiner, and he proved a number of remarkable properties of it. It seems that the best way to study the figure is by the inversion transformation. We content ourselves here with a proof of just one of Steiner's theorems. We first formulate a definition.

3.7.7   *Definition.*   A *Steiner chain of circles* is a sequence of circles, finite in number, each tangent to two fixed nonintersecting circles and to two other circles of the sequence.

3.7.8   *Steiner's Porism.*   *If two given nonintersecting circles admit a Steiner chain, they admit an infinite number, all of which contain the same number of circles, and any circle tangent to the two given circles and surrounding either none or both of them is a member of such a chain.*

The proof is simple. By Theorem 3.6.12, the two given circles may be inverted into a pair of concentric circles, the circles of the Steiner chain then becoming a Steiner chain of equal circles for the two concentric circles. Since the circles of this associated Steiner chain may each be advanced cyclically in the ring in which they lie to form a similar chain, and this can be done in infinitely many ways, the theorem follows.

Theorem 3.7.8 is representative of a whole class of propositions in which there is a condition for a certain relation to subsist, but if the condition holds then the relation subsists infinitely often. Such propositions are called *porisms.* Three books of porisms by Euclid have been lost.

PEAUCELLIER'S CELL

An outstanding geometrical problem of the last half of the nineteenth century was to discover a linkage mechanism for drawing a straight line. A solution was finally found in 1864 by a French army officer, A. Peaucellier (1832-1913), and an announcement of the invention was made by A. Mannheim (1831 - 1906), a brother officer of engineers and inventor of the so-called Mannheim slide rule, at a meeting of the Paris Philomathic Society in 1867. But the announcement was little heeded until Lipkin, a young student of the celebrated Russian mathematician Chebyshev (1821 - 1894), independently reinvented the mechanism in 1871. Chebyshev had been trying to demonstrate the impossibility of such a mechanism. Lipkin received a substantial reward from the Russian Government, whereupon Peucellier's merit was finally recognized and he was awarded the great mechanical prize of the Institut de France. Peaucellier's instrument contains 7 bars. In 1874 Harry Hart (1848 - 1920) discovered a 5-bar linkage for drawing straight lines, and no one has since been able to reduce this number of links or to prove that a further reduction is impossible. Both Peaucellier's and Hart's linkages are based upon the fact that the inverse of a circle through the center of inversion is a straight line.

The subject of linkages became quite fashionable among geometers, and many linkages were found for constructing special curves, such as conics, cardioids, lemniscates, and cissoids. In 1933, R. Kanayama published (in the *Tôhoku Mathematics Journal*, Vol. 37, 1933, pp. 294 - 319), a bibliography of 306 titles of papers and works on linkage mechanisms written between 1631 and 1931. It has been shown (in *Scripta Mathematica*, Vol. 2, 1934, pp. 293 - 294) that this list is far from complete, and of course many additional papers have appeared since 1931.

It has been proved that there exists a linkage for drawing any given algebraic curve, but that there cannot exist a linkage for drawing any transcendental curve. Linkages have been devised for mechanically solving algebraic equations.

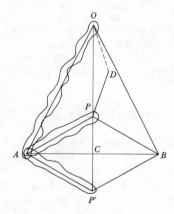

FIG. 3.7e

3.7.9 *Peaucellier's Cell. In Fig. 3.7e, let the points A and B of the jointed rhombus PAP'B be joined to the fixed point O by means of equal bars OA and OB, OA > PA. Then, if all points of the figure are free to move except point O, the points P and P' will describe inverse curves under the inversion I(O, OA² − PA²). In particular, if a seventh bar DP, DP > OP/2, is attached to P and the point D fixed so that DO = DP, then P' will describe a straight line.*

For, clearly, O, P, P' are collinear and

$$(OP)(OP') = (OC - PC)(OC + PC)$$
$$= OC^2 - PC^2$$

$$= (OC^2 + CA^2) - (PC^2 + CA^2)$$
$$= OA^2 - PA^2.$$

PROBLEMS

3.7-1   Draw the figure obtained by inverting three pairwise orthogonal circles with respect to a point of intersection of two of the circles.

3.7-2   Let $T_1 T_2 T_3 T_4$ be a convex quadrilateral inscribed in a circle C. Let C_1, C_2, C_3, C_4 be four circles touching circle C externally at T_1, T_2, T_3, T_4 respectively. Show that

$$t_{12} t_{34} + t_{23} t_{41} = t_{13} t_{24},$$

where t_{ij} is the length of a common external tangent to circles C_i and C_j. (This is a special case of a more general theorem due to Casey. It can be considered as a generalization of Ptolemy's Theorem.)

3.7-3   If PQ, RS are common tangents to two circles PAR, QAS, prove that the circles PAQ, RAS are tangent to each other.

3.7-4   (a)   Invert with respect to the center of the semicircle the theorem: An angle inscribed in a semicircle is a right angle.
(b)   Invert with respect to A the theorem: If A, B, C, D are concyclic points, then angles ABD, ACD are equal or supplementary.

3.7-5   Given a triangle ABC and a point M. Draw the circles MBC, MCA, MAB, and then draw the tangents to these circles at M to cut BC, CA, AB in R, S, T. Prove that R, S, T are collinear.

3.7-6   Circles K_1, K_2 touch each other at T, and a variable circle through T cuts K_1, K_2 orthogonally in X_1, X_2, respectively. Prove that $X_1 X_2$ passes through a fixed point.

3.7-7 A, B, C, D are four concyclic points. If a circle through A and B touches one through C and D, prove that the locus of the point of contact is a circle.

3.7-8 AC is a diameter of a given circle, and chords AB, CD intersect (produced if necessary) in a point O. Prove that circle OBD is orthogonal to the given circle.

3.7-9 If a quadrilateral with sides a, b, c, x is inscribed in a semicircle of diameter x, show that

$$x^3 - (a^2 + b^2 + c^2)x - 2abc = 0.$$

3.7-10 Prove Theorem 3.7.2.

3.7-11 Prove Ptolemy's Second Theorem: If $ABCD$ is a convex quadrilateral inscribed in a circle, then

$$AC/BD = (AB \cdot AD + CB \cdot CD)/(BA \cdot BC + DA \cdot DC).$$

3.7-12 (a) If A', B' are the inverses of A, B, then show that AA', BB' are antiparallel relative to AB and $A'B'$.

(b) If A, B, C, D are four points such that AB and CD are antiparallel relative to AD and BC, show that the four points can be inverted into the vertices of a rectangle.

3.7-13 Fill in the details of the proof of Theorem 3.7.6.

3.7-14 Show that the points of contact of the circles of a Steiner chain of circles all lie on a circle.

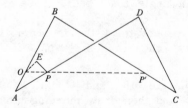

FIG. 3.7f

3.7-15 A linkage, called *Hart's contraparallelogram* (invented by H. Hart in 1874) is pictured in Fig. 3.7f. The four rods AB, CD, BC, DA, $AB = CD$, $BC = DA$, are hinged at A, B, C, D. If O, P, P' divide AB, AD, CB proportionately, and the linkage is pivoted at O, show that O, P, P' are always collinear and that P and P' describe inverse curves with respect to O as center of the inversion. Hence if a fifth rod $EP > OP/2$ be pivoted at E with $OE = EP$, P' will describe a straight line.

3.8   RECIPROCATION

We now consider a remarkable transformation of the set S of all points of the extended plane onto the set T of all straight lines of the extended plane.

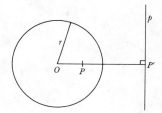

FIG. 3.8a

3.8.1   *Definitions and Notation.*   Let $O(r)$ be a fixed circle (see Fig. 3.8a) and let P be any ordinary point other than O. Let P' be the inverse of P in circle $O(r)$. Then the line p through P' and perpendicular to OPP' is called the *polar* of P for the circle $O(r)$. The *polar of O* is taken as the line at infinity, and the *polar of an ideal point* P is taken as the line through O perpendicular to the direction OP.

If line p is the polar of point P, then point P is called the *pole* of line p.

The pole–polar transformation set up by circle $K = O(r)$ will be denoted by $P(K)$ or $P(O(r))$ and will be called *reciprocation* in circle K.

Some nascent properties of reciprocation may be found in the works of Apollonius and Pappus. The theory was considerably developed by Desargues in his treatise on conic sections of 1639, and by his student Philippe de La Hire (1640 - 1718), and then greatly elaborated in the first half of the nineteenth century in connection with the study of the conic sections in projective geometry. The term *pole* was introduced in 1810 by the French mathematician F. J. Servois, and the corresponding term *polar* by Gergonne two to three years later. Gergonne and Poncelet developed reciprocation into a regular method out of which grew the elegant *principle of duality* of projective geometry. We shall look into this matter in Chap. V.

The easy proof of the following theorem is left to the reader.

3.8.2   *Theorem.*   (1) *The polar of a point for a circle intersects the circle, is tangent to the circle at the point, or does not intersect the circle, according as the point is outside, on, or inside the circle.* (2) *If point* P *is outside a circle, then its polar for the circle passes through the points of of contact of the tangents to the circle from* P.

The next theorem is basic in applications of reciprocation.

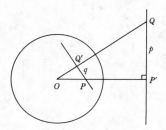

FIG. 3.8b

3.8.3   *Theorem.*   (1) *If, for a given circle, the polar of* P *passes through* Q, *then the polar of* Q *passes through* P. (2) *If, for a given circle, the pole of line* p *lies on line* q, *then the pole of* q *lies on* p. (3) *If, for a given circle,* P *and* Q *are the poles of* p *and* q, *then the pole of line* PQ *is the point of intersection of* p *and* q.

(1)   Suppose that P and Q are ordinary points. Let P' (see Fig. 3.8b) be the inverse of P and Q' the inverse of Q in the given circle, and suppose that P' and Q are distinct. Then $\overline{OP} \cdot \overline{OP'} = \overline{OQ} \cdot \overline{OQ'}$, whence P, P', Q, Q' are concyclic and $\measuredangle PP'Q = \measuredangle PQ'O$. But, since Q lies on the polar of P, $\measuredangle PP'Q = 90°$. Therefore $\measuredangle PQ'O = 90°$, and P lies on the polar of Q. If $P' = Q$, the theorem is obvious. The cases where P, or Q, or both P and Q are ideal points are easily handled.

(2)   Let P and Q be the poles of p and q. It is given that q (the polar of Q) passes through P. It follows, by (1), that p (the polar of P) passes through Q.

(3)   Let p and q intersect in R. Then the polar of P passes through R, whence the polar of R passes through P. Similarly, the polar of R passes through Q. Therefore line PQ is the polar of R.

3.8.4   *Corollary.*   *The polars, for a given circle, of a range of points constitute a pencil of lines; the poles, for a given circle, of a pencil of lines constitute a range of points.*

3.8.5   *Definitions.*   Two points such that each lies on the polar of the other, for a given circle, are called *conjugate points* for the circle; two lines such that each passes through the pole of the other, for a given circle, are called *conjugate lines* for the circle.

The reader should find no difficulty in establishing the following facts.

3.8.6 *Theorem. For a given circle:* (1) *Each point of a line has a conjugate point on that line.* (2) *Each line through a point has a conjugate line through that point.* (3) *Of two distinct conjugate points on a line that cuts the circle, one is inside and the other outside the circle.* (4) *Of two distinct conjugate lines that intersect outside the circle, one cuts the circle and the other does not.* (5) *Any point on the circle is conjugate to all the points on the tangent to the circle at the point.* (6) *Any tangent to the circle is conjugate to all lines through its point of contact with the circle.*

The next few theorems will be found important in the projective theory of poles and polars.

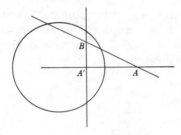

FIG. 3.8c

3.8.7 *Theorem. If, for a given circle, two conjugate points lie on a line which intersects the circle, they are harmonically separated by the points of intersection.*

Let A and B (see Fig. 3.8c) be two such points, and let A' be the inverse of A in the circle. If $B = A'$, the desired result follows immediately. If $B \neq A'$, then $A'B$ is the polar of A and $\angle AA'B = 90°$. The circle on AB as diameter, since it passes through A', is (by Theorem 3.5.8) orthogonal to the given circle. It follows (by Theorem 2.6.3) that A and B are harmonically separated by the points in which their line intersects the circle.

3.8.8 *Corollary. If a variable line through a given point intersects a circle, the harmonic conjugates of the point with respect to the intersections of the line and circle all lie on the polar of the given point.*

3.8.9 *Theorem. If, for a given circle, two conjugate lines intersect outside the circle, they are harmonically separated by the tangents to the circle from their point of intersection.*

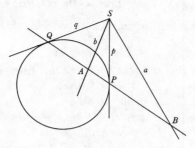

FIG. 3.8d

Let a and b (see Fig. 3.8d) be two such lines and let S be their point of intersection. Since a and b are conjugate lines for the circle, the pole A of a lies on b, and the pole B of b lies on a. Then (by Theorem 3.8.3(3)) line AB is the polar of S and must pass through the points P and Q where the tangents from S touch the circle. Now A and B are conjugate points, whence (by Theorem 3.8.7) $(AB, PQ) = -1$. It follows that $(ba, pq) = -1$.

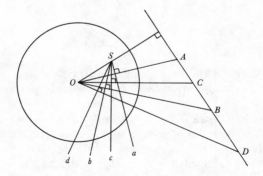

FIG. 3.8e

3.8.10   *Theorem.   If* A, B, C, D *are four distinct collinear points, and* a, b, c, d *are their polars for a given circle, then* (AB,CD) = (ab,cd).

Referring to Fig. 3.8e, the polars a, b, c, d all pass through S, the pole of the line $ABCD$. Since each polar is perpendicular to the line joining its pole to the center O of the circle, we see that

$$(ab,cd) = O(AB,CD) = (AB,CD).$$

We conclude with a few applications of the theory of poles and polars. The first is a proof of Brianchon's Theorem for a circle (see Problem 2.4-6). This theorem was discovered and published in a paper by C. J. Brianchon (1785 - 1864) in 1806, when still a student at the École Polytechnique in Paris, over 150 years after Pascal had stated his famous mystic-hexagram theorem. Brianchon's paper was one of the first publications to employ reciprocation to obtain new geometrical results, and his theorem played a leading role in the recognition of the far-reaching principle of duality. The following proof of Brianchon's Theorem is essentially that given by Brianchon himself.

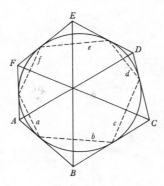

FIG. 3.8f

3.8.11 *Brianchon's Theorem for a Circle. If a hexagon (not necessarily convex) is circumscribed about a circle, the three lines joining pairs of opposite vertices are concurrent.*

Let *ABCDEF* (see Fig. 3.8f) be a hexagon circumscribed about a circle. The polars for the circle, of the vertices *A, B, C, D, E, F,* form the sides *a, b, c, d, e, f* of an inscribed hexagon. Since *a* is the polar of *A* and *d* the polar of *D*, the point *ad* is (by Theorem 3.8.3(3)) the pole of line *AD*. Similarly, the point *be* is the pole of line *BE*, and the point *cf* is the pole of line *CF*. Now, by Pascal's "mystic-hexagram" theorem, the points *ad, be, cf* are collinear. It follows (by Theorem 3.8.4) that the polars *AD, BE, CF* are concurrent.

3.8.12 *Theorem. Let ABCD be a complete quadrangle inscribed in a circle. Then each diagonal point of the quadrangle is the pole, for the circle, of the line determined by the other two diagonal points.*

For we have (see Fig. 3.8g) $(AD,MQ) = (BC,NQ) = -1$, whence (by Corollary 3.8.8) line PR is the polar of point Q. Similarly line QR is the polar of point P. It then follows (by Theorem 3.8.3(3)) that line PQ is the polar of point R.

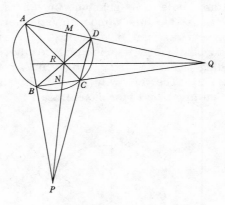

FIG. 3.8g

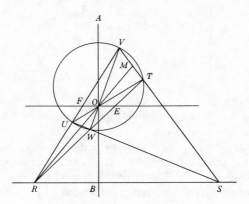

FIG. 3.8h

3.8.13   *The Butterfly Theorem.   Let* O *be the midpoint of a given chord of a circle, let two other chords* TU *and* VW *be drawn through* O, *and let* TW *and* VU *cut the given chord in* E *and* F, *respectively. Then* O *is the midpoint of* FE.

If the given chord is a diameter of the circle, the theorem is obvious. Otherwise (see Fig. 3.8h) produce TW and VU to intersect in R, and VT and UW to intersect in S. Then (by Theorem 3.8.12)

RS is the polar of O, whence RS is perpendicular to the diametral line AOB. But FE is perpendicular to AOB. Therefore FE is parallel to RS. Now (by Theorem 2.5.11) $R(VT,MS) = -1$, whence $(FE,O \infty) = -1$, and O bisects FE.

Theorem 3.8.13 has received its name from the fancied resemblance of the figure of the theorem to a butterfly with outspread wings. It is a real stickler if one is limited to the use of only high school geometry.

PROBLEMS

3.8-1   Establish Theorem 3.8.2.

3.8-2   Establish Theorem 3.8.6.

3.8-3   If P and Q are conjugate points for a circle, show that $(PQ)^2$ is equal to the sum of the powers of P and Q with respect to the circle.

3.8-4   If PR is a diameter of a circle K_1 orthogonal to a circle K_2 of center O, and if OP meets K_1 in Q, prove that line QR is the polar of P for K_2.

3.8-5   A variable chord PQ of a given circle K passes through a fixed point T. Prove that the tangents at P and Q intersect on a fixed line t.

3.8-6   (a)   If P and Q are conjugate points for circle K, prove that the circle on PQ as diameter is orthogonal to K.
(b)   If two circles are orthogonal, prove that the extremities of any diameter of one are conjugate points for the other.

3.8-7   (a)   Let K_1, K_2, K_3 be three circles having a radical circle R, and let P be any point on R. Show that the polars of P for K_1, K_2, K_3 are concurrent.
(b)   A common tangent to two circles K_1 and K_2 touches them at P and Q, respectively. Show that P and Q are conjugate points for any circle coaxial with K_1 and K_2.
(c)   The tangent to the circumcircle of triangle ABC at vertex A intersects line BC at T and is produced to U so that $AT = TU$. Prove that A and U are conjugate points for any circle passing through B and C.
(d)   Let ABC be a right triangle with right angle at B, and let B' be the midpoint of AC. Prove that A and C are conjugate points for any circle which touches BB' at B.

(e) If a pair of opposite vertices of a square are conjugate points for a circle, prove that the other pair of opposite vertices are also conjugate points for the circle.

3.8-8 Prove Salmon's Theorem: If P, Q are two points, and PX, QY are the perpendiculars from P, Q to the polars of Q, P, respectively, for a circle of center O, then $OP/OQ = PX/QY$.

3.8-9 Consider the two propositions: (1) The lines joining the vertices of a triangle to the points of contact of the opposite sides with the incircle of the triangle are concurrent. (2) The tangents to the circumcircle of a triangle at the vertices of the triangle meet the opposite sides of the triangle in three collinear points.

Show that Proposition (2) can be obtained from Proposition (1) by subjecting Proposition (1) to a reciprocation in the incircle of the triangle.

3.8-10 (a) Let PQR be a triangle and let P', Q', R' be the poles of QR, RP, PQ for a circle K. Show that P, Q, R are the poles of $Q'R', R'P, P'Q'$ for circle K. (Two triangles such that the vertices of either are poles for a given circle of the sides of the other are called a pair of *conjugate triangles* for the circle. If a triangle is conjugate to itself — that is, each vertex is the pole of the opposite side — the triangle is said to be *self-conjugate*, or *self-polar*, for the circle.)

(b) If P, Q are two conjugate points for a circle, and R is the pole of PQ, show that PQR is a self-conjugate triangle.

(c) If a triangle is self-conjugate for a circle, prove that its orthocenter is the center of the circle.

(d) Given an obtuse triangle, prove that there exists one and only one circle for which the triangle is self-conjugate. (The circle for which an obtuse triangle is self-conjugate is called the *polar circle* of the triangle.)

(e) Prove that the polar circle of an obtuse triangle ABC has its center at the orthocenter of the triangle, and its radius equal to $[(\overline{HA})(\overline{HD})]^{1/2}$, where D is the foot of the altitude from A.

(f) Prove that the inverse of the circumcircle of an obtuse triangle with respect to its polar circle is the nine-point circle of the triangle.

3.8-11 (a) Prove in Fig. 3.8g, that triangle PQR is self-conjugate for the circle $ABCD$.

(b) Show that the circles on PQ, QR, RP as diameters are orthogonal to the circle $ABCD$.

3.8-12 Prove that two conjugate triangles for a circle are copolar.

3.8-13 Prove Hesse's Theorem for a Circle (1840): If two pairs of opposite vertices of a complete quadrilateral are conjugate points for a circle, then the third pair of opposite vertices are also conjugate points for the circle.

IV. EUCLIDEAN
CONSTRUCTIONS

There is much to be said in favor of a game which you play alone. It can be played or abandoned whenever you wish. There is no bother about securing a willing and suitable opponent, nor do you annoy anyone if you suddenly decide to desist play. Since you are, in a sense, your own opponent, the company is most congenial and perfectly matched in skill and intelligence, and there is no embarrassing sarcastic utterance should you make a stupid play. The game is particularly good if it is truly challenging and if it possesses manifold variety. It is still better if also the rules of the game are very few and simple. And little more can be asked if, in addition, the game requires no highly specialized equipment, and so can be played almost anywhere and at almost any time.

The Greek geometers of antiquity devised a game — we might call it *geometrical solitaire* — which, judged on all the above points, must surely stand at the very top of any list of games to be played alone. Over the ages it has attracted hosts of players, and though now well over 2000 years old, it seems not to have lost any of its singular charm and appeal. This chapter is concerned with a few facets of this fascinating game, and with some of its interesting modern variants.

4.1   THE EUCLIDEAN TOOLS

We here state the first three postulates of Euclid's *Elements*:

   1. A straight line segment can be drawn connecting any point to any other point.
   2. A straight line segment can be produced continuously in a straight line.
   3. A circle can be drawn with any point as center and with any straight line segment radiating from that center as a radius.

These postulates state the primitive constructions from which all other constructions in the *Elements* are to be compounded. They constitute, so to speak, the rules of the game of Euclidean construction. Since they restrict constructions to only those that can be made in a permissible way with straightedge and compass,* these two instruments, so limited, are known as the *Euclidean tools*.

The first two postulates tell us what we can do with a Euclidean straightedge; we are permitted to draw as much as may be desired of the straight line determined by any two given points. The third postulate tells us what we can do with the Euclidean compass; we are permitted to draw the circle of given center and passing through a given point. Note that neither instrument is to be used for transferring distances. This means that the straightedge cannot be marked, and the compass must be regarded as having the characteristic that if either leg is lifted from the paper, the instrument immediately collapses. For this reason, a Euclidean compass is often referred to as a *collapsing compass*; it differs from a *modern compass*, which retains its opening and hence can be used as a divider for transferring distances.

It would seem that a modern compass might be more powerful than a collapsing compass. Curiously enough, such turns out not to be the case; any construction performable with a modern compass can also be carried out (in perhaps a longer way) by means of a collapsing compass. We prove this fact as our first theorem, right after introducing the following convenient notation.

   4.1.1 *Notation.*   The circle with center O and passing through a given point C will be denoted by $O(C)$, and the circle with center O and radius equal to a given segment AB will be denoted by $O(AB)$.

   4.1.2 *Theorem.   The collapsing and modern compasses are equivalent.*

To prove the theorem it suffices to show that we may, with a collapsing compass, construct any circle $O(AB)$. This may be accomplished as follows (see Fig. 4.1a). Draw circles $A(O)$ and $O(A)$ to intersect in D and E; draw circles $D(B)$ and $E(B)$ to

---

*Though contrary to common English usage, we shall use this word in the singular.

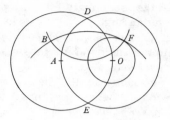

FIG. 4.1a

intersect again in F; draw circle $O(F)$. It is an easy matter to prove that $OF = AB$, whence circle $O(F)$ is the same as circle $O(AB)$.

In view of Theorem 4.1.2, we may dispense with the Euclidean, or collapsing compass, and in its place employ the more convenient modern compass. We are assured that the set of constructions performable with straightedge and Euclidean compass is the same as the set performable with straightedge and modern compass. As a matter of fact, in all our construction work, we shall not be interested in actually and exactly carrying out the constructions, but merely in assuring ourselves that such constructions are possible. To use a phrase of Jacob Steiner, we shall do our constructions "simply by means of the tongue," rather than with actual instruments on paper. We seek, then, the easiest construction to describe rather than the simplest or best construction actually to carry out with the instruments.

If one were asked to find the midpoint of a given line segment using only the straightedge, one would be justified in exclaiming that surely the Euclidean straightedge alone will not suffice, and that some additional tool or permission must be furnished. The same is true of the combined Euclidean tools; there are constructions which cannot be performed with these tools alone, at least under the restrictions imposed upon them. Three famous problems of this sort, which originated in ancient Greece, are:

(1) *The duplication of the cube,* or the problem of constructing the edge of a cube having twice the volume of a given cube.

(2) *The trisection of an angle,* or the problem of dividing a given arbitrary angle into three equal parts.

(3) *The quadrature of the circle,* or the problem of constructing a square having an area equal to that of a given circle.

But, in spite of the limited power of our instruments, one is surprised at the really intricate constructions that can be accomplished with them. Thus, though with our instruments we cannot, for example, solve the seemingly simple problem of drawing the two lines trisecting an angle of $60°$, we can draw all the circles which touch three given circles (the *problem of Apollonius*); we can draw three circles in the angles of a triangle such that each circle touches the other two and also the two sides of the angle (the *problem of Malfatti*); we can inscribe in a given circle a triangle whose sides, produced if necessary, pass through three given points (the *Castillon-Cramer problem*).

As a concluding remark of this section we point out that Euclid used constructions in the sense of existence theorems — to prove that certain entities actually exist. Thus one may define a *bisector* of a given angle as a line in the plane of the angle, passing through the vertex of the angle, and such that it divides the given angle into two equal angles. But a definition does not establish the existence of the thing being defined; this requires proof. To show that a given angle does possess a bisector, we show that this entity can actually be constructed. Existence theorems are very important in mathematics, and actual construction of an entity is the most satisfying way of proving its existence. One might define a *square circle* as a figure which is both a square and a circle, but one would never be able to prove that such an entity exists; the class of square circles is a class without any members. In mathematics it is nice to know that the set of entities satisfying a certain definition is not just the empty set.

PROBLEMS

4.1-1   In the proof of Theorem 4.1.2, show that $OF = AB$.

4.1-2   A student reading Euclid's *Elements* for the first time might experience surprise at the three opening propositions of Book I:

1. To construct an equilateral triangle on a given straight line segment.
2. From a given point to draw a straight line segment equal to a given straight line segment.
3. From the greater of two given unequal straight line segments to cut off a part equal to the less.

These three propositions are constructions, and are trivial with straightedge and *modern* compass, but require some ingenuity with straightedge and *Euclidean* compass.
(a)   Solve I 1 with Euclidean tools.

(b)   Solve I 2 with Euclidean tools.

(c)   Solve I 3 with Euclidean tools.

(d)   Show that I 2 proves that the straightedge and Euclidean compass are equivalent to the straightedge and modern compass.

4.1-3   Consider the following two arguments:

I.   Theorem.   *Of all triangles inscribed in a circle, the equilateral is the greatest.*

1. If ABC is a nonequilateral triangle inscribed in a circle, so that $AB \neq AC$, say, construct triangle XBC, where X is the intersection of the perpendicular bisector of BC with arc BAC.

2. Then triangle XBC > triangle ABC.

3. Hence, if we have a nonequilateral triangle inscribed in a circle, we can always construct a greater inscribed triangle.

4. Therefore, of all triangles inscribed in a circle, the equilateral is the greatest.

II.   Theorem.   *Of all natural numbers, 1 is the greatest.*

1. If m is a natural number other than 1, construct the natural number m^2.

2. Then $m^2 > m$.

3. Hence, if we have a natural number other than 1, we can always construct a greater natural number.

4. Therefore, of all natural numbers, 1 is the greatest.

Now the conclusion in argument I is true, and that in argument II is false. But the two arguments are formally identical. What, then, is wrong?

4.2 THE METHOD OF LOCI AND THE METHOD OF TRANS-FORMATION

In this section we very briefly consider two methods which have proved to be highly useful in the solution of geometric construction problems. They may be considered as maneuvers in the construction game.

The solution of a construction problem very often depends upon first finding some key point. Thus the problem of drawing a circle through three given points is essentially solved once the center of the circle is located. Again, the problem of drawing a tangent to a circle from an external point is essentially solved once the point of contact of the tangent with the circle has been found. Now the key point satisfies certain conditions, and each condition considered alone generally restricts the position of the key point to a certain locus. The key point is thus found at the intersections of certain loci. This method of solving a construction problem is aptly referred to as the *method of loci*.

To illustrate, denote the three given points in our first problem above by A, B, C. Now the sought center O of the circle through A, B, C must be equidistant from A and B and also from B and C. The first condition places O on the perpendicular bisector of AB, and the second condition places O on the perpendicular bisector of BC. The point O is thus found at the intersection, if it exists, of these two perpendicular bisectors. If the three given points are not collinear, there is exactly one solution; otherwise there is none.

Suppose that, in our second problem above, we denote the center of the given circle by O, the external point by E, and the sought point of contact of the tangent from E to the circle by T. Now T, first of all, lies on the given circle. Also, since $\angle OTE = 90°$, T lies on the circle having OE as diameter. The sought point T is thus found at an intersection of these two circles. There are always two solutions to the problem.

In order to apply the method of loci to the solution of geometric constructions, it is evidently of great value to know a considerable number of loci that are straight lines and circles. We consider one further example of this method, wherein the loci are circles of Apollonius (see Corollary 3.3.10).

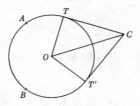

FIG. 4.2a

4.2.1 *Problem. Draw a circle passing through two given points and subtending a given angle at a third point.*

Referring to Fig. 4.2a, let A and B be the two given points and let C be the third point. Denote the center of the sought circle by O and let T and T' denote the points of contact of the tangents to the circle from point C. Since $\angle TCT'$ is given, the form of right triangle OTC is known. That is, we know the ratio OT/OC. But

$OA/OC = OB/OC = OT/OC$. It follows that O lies on the circle of Apollonius for A and C and ratio OT/OC, and on the circle of Apollonius for B and C and ratio OT/OC. Point O is thus found at the intersections, if any exist, of these two circles of Apollonius. The details are left to the reader.

There are many geometric construction problems that can be solved by applying one of the transformations discussed in the previous chapter. We illustrate this method of transformation by the following sequence of problems, in which certain details are left to the reader.

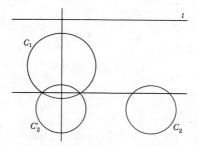

FIG. 4.2b

4.2.2   *Problem.   Draw a line in a given direction on which two given circles cut off equal chords.*

In Fig. 4.2b, let C_1 and C_2 be the two given circles and let t be a line in the given direction. Translate C_2 parallel to t to position C'_2 in which the line of centers of C_1 and C'_2 is perpendicular to t. Then the line through the points of intersection, if such exist, of C_1 and C'_2 is the sought line.

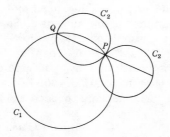

FIG. 4.2c

4.2.3 *Problem. Through one of the points of intersection of two given intersecting circles, draw a line on which the two circles cut off equal chords.*

In Fig. 4.2c, let C_1 and C_2 be the two given intersecting circles, and let P be one of the points of intersection. Reflect C_2 in point P into position C'_2 and let Q be the other intersection of C_1 and C'_2. Then QP is the sought line.

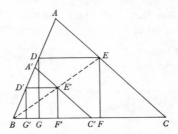

FIG. 4.2d

4.2.4 *Problem. Inscribe a square in a given triangle, so that one side of the square lies on a given side of the triangle.*

In Fig. 4.2d, let ABC be the given triangle and BC the side on which the required square is to lie. Choose any point D' on side AB and construct the square $D'E'F'G'$ as indicated in the figure. If E' falls on AC, the problem is solved. Otherwise we have solved the problem for a triangle $A'BC'$ which is homothetic to triangle ABC with B as center of homothety. It follows that line BE' cuts AC in vertex E of the sought square inscribed in triangle ABC.

It is interesting, in connection with the last problem, to contemplate that from a sheer guess of the position of the sought square we were able to find the actual position of the square. The method employed, often called the *method of similitude,* is a geometric counterpart of the *rule of false position* used by the ancient Egyptians to solve linear equations in one unknown. Suppose, for example, that we are to solve the simple equation $x + x/5 = 24$. Assume any convenient value of x, say $x = 5$. Then $x + x/5 = 6$, instead of 24. Since 6 must be multiplied by 4 to give the required 24, the correct value of x must be 4(5), or 20. From a sheer guess, and without employment of algebraic procedures, we have obtained the correct answer.

4.2.5 *A General Problem. Given a point* O *and two curves* C_1 *and* C_2. *Locate a triangle* OP_1P_2, *where* P_1 *is on* C_1 *and* P_2 *is on* C_2, *similar to a given triangle* $O'P'_1P'_2$.

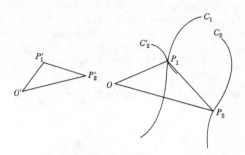

FIG. 4.2e

In Fig. 4.2e, let C'_2 be the map of C_2 under the homology

$$H(O, \ \measuredangle \ P'_2 O' P'_1 , \ O' P'_1 / O' P'_2).$$

Then C_1 and C'_2 intersect in the possible positions of P_1. If C_1 and C_2 are "circles," the problem can be solved with Euclidean tools.

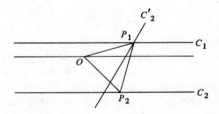

FIG. 4.2f

4.2.6   *Problem.   Draw an equilateral triangle having its three vertices on three given parallel lines.*

In Fig. 4.2f, choose any point O on one of the three given parallel lines, and denote the other two parallel lines by C_1 and C_2. We may now apply the General Problem 4.2.5, by subjecting line C_2 to the homology $H(O, 60°, 1)$.

4.2.7   *Problem.   Draw a "circle" touching three given concurrent non-coaxial circles.*

In Fig. 4.2g, let the three given circles C_1, C_2, C_3 intersect in point O. Subject the figure to any convenient inversion of center O. Then C_1, C_2, C_3 become three straight lines C'_1, C'_2, C'_3, which are easily constructed with Euclidean tools (they are actually the

common chords of C_1, C_2, C_3 with the circle of inversion). Draw
a circle C' touching all three of the lines C'_1, C'_2, C'_3. The inverse
C of this circle, which can be constructed with Euclidean tools
(if C' touches C'_1, C'_2, C'_3 at P'_1, P'_2, P'_3, respectively, then C
touches C_1, C_2, C_3 at the points P_1, P_2, P_3 where OP'_1, OP'_2, OP'_3
cut C_1, C_2, C_3 again), is a "circle" touching C_1, C_2, C_3. Note that
there are four solutions to the problem.

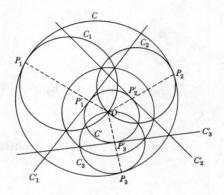

FIG. 4.2g

The *method of homology*, illustrated in Problem 4.2.6, and the
method of inversion, illustrated in Problem 4.2.7, are powerful
methods, and many construction problems that would otherwise be
very difficult yield to these methods. They are, of course, instances
of the general method of transformation. Note that Problem 4.2.7
is a special case of the Problem of Apollonius.

PROBLEMS

4.2-1   Complete the details of Problem 4.2.1.

4.2-2   Construct a triangle given one side and the altitude and
        median to that side.

4.2-3   Draw a circle touching two given parallel lines and
        passing through a given point.

4.2-4   Construct a triangle given one side, the opposite angle,
        and the median to the given side.

4.2-5   Find a point at which three given circles subtend equal angles.

4.2-6   Two balls are placed on a diameter of a circular billiard table. How must one ball be played in order to hit the other after its recoil from the circumference?

4.2-7   Through two given points of a circle draw two parallel chords whose sum shall have a given length.

4.2-8   Draw a circle of given radius touching a given circle and having its center on a given line.

4.2-9   Inscribe a right triangle in a given circle so that each leg will pass through a given point.

4.2-10   Draw a circle tangent to a given line at a given point and also tangent to a given circle.

4.2-11   Place a line segment equal and parallel to a given line segment and having its extremities on two given circles.

4.2-12   From a vessel two known points are seen under a given angle. The vessel sails a given distance in a known direction, and now the same two points are seen under another known angle. Find the position of the vessel.

4.2-13   Solve the general problem: To a given line draw a perpendicular on which two given curves will cut off equal lengths measured from the foot of the perpendicular.

4.2-14   Place a square with two opposite vertices on a given line and the other two vertices on two given circles.

4.2-15   Draw a triangle given the positions of three points which divide the three sides in given ratios.

4.2-16   Find points D and E on sides AB and AC of a triangle ABC so that $BD = DE = EC$.

4.2-17   Draw a triangle given $A, a + b, a + c$.

4.2-18   Solve the general problem: Through a given point O draw a line intersecting two given curves C_1 and C_2 in points P_1 and P_2 so that OP_1 and OP_2 shall be in a given ratio to one another.

4.2-19   Through a given point O on a given circle draw a chord which is bisected by another given chord.

4.2-20   Two radii are drawn in a circle. Draw a chord which will be trisected by the radii.

4.2-21   Draw an equilateral triangle having its three vertices on three given concentric circles.

4.2-22   Solve the general problem: Through a given point O draw a line cutting two given curves C_1 and C_2 in points P_1 and P_2 such that $(OP_1)(OP_2)$ is a given constant.

4.2-23   Through a given point O draw a line cutting two given lines in points A and B so that $(OA)(OB)$ is given.

4.2-24   Draw a circle passing through a given point P and touching two given circles.

4.2-25   Draw a circle through two given points and tangent to a given circle.

4.2-26   Draw a circle tangent externally to three given mutually external circles.

4.3   THE MOHR–MASCHERONI CONSTRUCTION THEOREM

The eighteenth-century Italian geometer and poet Lorenzo Mascheroni (1750-1800) made the surprising discovery that all Euclidean constructions, insofar as the given and required elements are points, can be made with the compass alone, and that the straightedge is thus a redundant tool. Of course, straight lines cannot be drawn with the compass, but any straight line arrived at in a Euclidean construction can be determined by the compass by finding two points on the line. This discovery appeared in 1797 in Mascheroni's *Geometria del compasso.*   Generally speaking, Mascheroni established his results by using the idea of reflection in a line. In 1890, the Viennese geometer August Adler (1863-1923) published a new proof of Mascheroni's results, using the inversion transformation.

Then an unexpected thing happened. Shortly before 1928, a student of the Danish mathematician Johannes Hjelmslev (1873-1950), while browsing in a bookstore in Copenhagen, came across a copy of an old book, *Euclides Danicus,* published in 1672 by an obscure writer named Georg Mohr. Upon examining the book, Hjelmslev was surprised to find that it contained Mascheroni's discovery, with a different solution, arrived at a hundred and twenty-five years before Mascheroni's publication had appeared.

The present section will be devoted to a proof of the Mohr-Mascheroni discovery. We shall employ the Mascheroni approach, and shall relegate Adler's approach to the problems at the end of the section. We first introduce a compact and elegant way of describing any given construction. The method will become clear from an example, and we choose the construction appearing in Theorem 4.1.2. That construction can be condensed into the following table:

$A(O)$, $O(A)$	$D(B)$, $E(B)$	$O(F)$
D, E	F	

The first line of the table tells us what "circles" we are to draw, and the second line labels the points of intersection so obtained. The table is divided vertically into steps. Reading the above table we have: Step 1. Draw circles $A(O)$ and $O(A)$ to intersect in points D and E. Step 2. Draw circles $D(B)$ and $E(B)$ to intersect in point F. Step 3. Draw circle $O(F)$. It will be noted that this is precisely the construction appearing in Theorem 4.1.2.

We are now ready to proceed.

4.3.1 *Problem.* *Given points* A, B, C, D, *construct, with a modern compass alone, the points of intersection of circle* C(D) *and line* AB.

Case 1. C not on AB (see Fig. 4.3a).

$A(C)$, $B(C)$	$C(D)$, $C_1(CD)$
C_1	X, Y

Case 2. C on AB (see Fig. 4.3b).

$A(D)$, $C(D)$	$C(DD_1)$, $D(C)$	$C(DD_1)$, $D_1(C)$	$F(D_1)$, $F_1(D)$	$F(CM)$, $C(D)$
D_1	F, 4th vertex of $\square CD_1DF$	F_1, 4th vertex of $\square CDD_1F_1$	M	X, Y

The proof of case 1 is easy. In case 2, observe (see Fig. 4.3b) that

$$(CM)^2 = (FM)^2 - 4a^2 = (FD_1)^2 - 4a^2 = (9a^2 + h^2) - 4a^2$$
$$= 9a^2 + r^2 - a^2 - 4a^2 = 4a^2 + r^2 = (FX)^2.$$

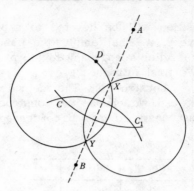

FIG . 4.3a

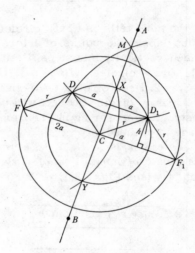

FIG . 4.3b

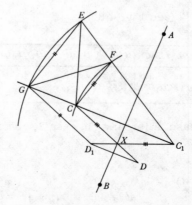

FIG . 4.3c

4.3.2   *Problem.   Given points* A, B, C, D, *construct with a modern compass alone, the points of intersection of the lines* AB *and* CD (see Fig. 4.3c).

$A(C), B(C)$	$A(D), B(D)$	$C(DD_1),$ $D_1(CD)$	$C_1(G), G(D_1)$	$C_1(C), G(CE)$	$C(F),$ $C_1(CF)$
C_1	D_1	G, collinear with C, C_1	E, either intersection	F, collinear with C_1, E	X

The proof is easy. We have $C_1 D_1 GE$ similar to $C_1 XCF$. But $GD_1 = GE$. Therefore $CX = CF$.

4.3.3   *The Mohr-Mascheroni Construction Theorem.   Any Euclidean construction, insofar as the given and required elements are points, may be accomplished with the Euclidean compass alone.*

For in a Euclidean construction, every new point is determined as an intersection of two circles, of a straight line and a circle, or of two straight lines, and the construction, no matter how complicated, is a succession of a finite number of these processes. Because of the equivalence of modern and Euclidean compasses (see Theorem 4.1.2), it is then sufficient to show that with a modern compass alone we are able to solve the following three problems:

I.   Given A, B, C, D, find the points of intersection of $A(B)$ and $C(D)$.

II.   Given A, B, C, D, find the points of intersection of AB and $C(D)$.

III.   Given A, B, C, D, find the point of intersection of AB and CD.

But I is obvious, and we have solved II and III in Problems 4.3.1 and 4.3.2, respectively.

It is to be noted that our proof of the Mohr-Mascheroni construction theorem is more than a mere existence proof, for not only have we shown the existence of a construction using only the Euclidean compass which can replace any given Euclidean construction, but we have shown how such a construction can actually be obtained from the given Euclidean construction. It must be confessed, though, that the resulting construction using only the Euclidean compass would, in all likelihood, be far more complicated than is necessary. The task of finding a "simplest" construction employing only the Euclidean compass, or even only the modern compass, is usually very difficult indeed, and requires considerable ingenuity on the part of the solver.

PROBLEMS

4.3-1 Solve or establish, as the case may be, the following constructions using only the *Euclidean* compass:

(a)   Given points A and B, find point C on AB produced such that $AB = BC$.

$B(A), A(B)$	$B(A), R(B)$	$B(A), S(B)$
R	S	C

(b)   Given points A and B, and a positive integer n, find point C on AB produced such that $AC = n(AB)$.

(c)   Given points O, A, B, find the reflection of O in line AB.

(d)   Given points O, D, M, find the inverse M' of M in circle $O(D)$.

Case 1. $OM > (OD)/2$.

$O(D), M(O)$	$A(O), B(O)$
A, B	M'

Case 2. $OM \leqq (OD)/2$.

(e)   Given noncollinear points A, B, O, find the center Q of the inverse of line AB in circle $O(D)$.

Find P, the reflection of O in AB, and then Q, the inverse of P in $O(D)$.

(f)   Given points O, D and a circle k not through O, find the center M' of the inverse k' of k in circle $O(D)$.

Find M, the inverse of O in k, and then M', the inverse of M in $O(D)$.

(g)   Given points A, B, C, D, construct, with a Euclidean compass alone, the points X, Y of intersection of circle $C(D)$ and line AB.

(h)   Given points A, B, C, D, construct, with a Euclidean compass alone, the point X of intersection of lines AB and CD.

The above steps essentially constitute Adler's proof of the Mohr-Mascheroni construction theorem. Note that Mascheroni's approach exploits reflections in lines whereas Adler's approach exploits the inversion transformation.

4.3-2   Establish the following solution, using a Euclidean compass

alone, of the problem of finding the center D of the circle
through three given noncollinear points A, B, C.

Draw circle $A(B)$. Find (by Problem 4.3-1 (d)) the inverse
C' of C in $A(B)$. Find (by Problem 4.3-1 (c)) the reflection
D' of A in BC'. Find (by Problem 4.3-1 (d)) the inverse D of
D' in $A(B)$.

4.3-3   Given points A and B, find, with a Euclidean compass
alone, the midpoint M of segment AB.

4.3-4   On page 268 of Cajori's *A History of Mathematics* we read:
"Napoleon proposed to the French mathematicians the problem,
to divide the circumference of a circle into four equal parts
by the compasses only. Mascheroni does this by applying the
radius three times to the circumference; he obtains the arcs
AB, BC, CD; then AD is a diameter; the rest is obvious."
Complete the "obvious" part of the construction.

4.4   THE PONCELET-STEINER CONSTRUCTION THEOREM

Though all Euclidean constructions, insofar as the given and
required elements are points, are possible with a Euclidean compass alone, it is an easy matter to assure ourselves that not all
Euclidean constructions are similarly possible with a Euclidean
straightedge alone. To see this, consider the problem of finding
the point M midway between two given points A and B, and suppose
that the problem can be solved with straightedge alone. That is,
suppose there exists a finite sequence of lines, drawn according
to the restrictions of Euclid's first two postulates, that finally
leads from the two given points A and B to the desired midpoint
M. Choose a point O outside the plane of construction, and from
O project the entire construction upon a second plane not through
O. Points A, B, M of the first plane project into points A', B', M'
of the second plane, and the sequence of lines leading to the point
M in the first plane projects into a sequence of lines leading to the
point M' in the second plane. The description of the straightedge
construction in the second plane, utilizing the projected sequence
of lines, of the point M' from the points A' and B' is exactly like
the description of the straightedge construction in the first plane,
utilizing the original sequence of lines, of the point M from the
points A and B. Since M is the midpoint of AB, it follows, then,
that M' must be the midpoint of $A'B'$. But this is absurd, for the
midpoint of a line segment need not project into the midpoint of

the projected segment. It follows that the simple Euclidean problem of finding the point M midway between two given points A and B is not possible with the straightedge alone.

Our inability to solve all Euclidean constructions with a straightedge alone shows that the straightedge must be assisted with the compass, or with some other tool. It is natural to wonder if the compass can be replaced by some kind of compass less powerful than the Euclidean and modern compasses. As early as the tenth century, the Arab mathematician Abû'1-Wefâ (940-998) considered constructions carried out with a straightedge and a so-called *rusty compass,* or a compass of fixed opening. Constructions of this sort appeared in Europe in the late fifteenth and early sixteenth centuries and engaged the attention of, among others, the great artists Albrecht Dürer (1471-1528) and Leonardo da Vinci (1452-1519). In this early work, the motivation was a practical one, and the radius of the rusty compass was chosen as some length convenient for the problem at hand. In the middle of the sixteenth century, a new viewpoint on the matter was adopted by Italian mathematicians. The motivation became a purely academic one, and the radius of the rusty compass was considered as arbitrarily assigned at the start. A number of writers showed how all the constructions in Euclid's *Elements* can be carried out with a straightedge and a given rusty compass. Some real ingenuity is required to accomplish this, as becomes evident to anyone who tries to construct with a straightedge and a rusty compass the triangle whose three sides are given.

But the fact that all the constructions in Euclid's *Elements* can be carried out with a straightedge and a given rusty compass does not prove that a straightedge and a rusty compass are together equivalent to a straightedge and a Euclidean compass. This equivalence was first indicated in 1822 by Victor Poncelet, who stated, with a suggested method of proof, that all Euclidean constructions can be carried out with the straightedge alone in the presence of a single circle and its center. This implies that all Euclidean constructions can be carried out with a straightedge and a rusty compass, and that, moreover, the rusty compass need be used *only once,* and thenceforth discarded. In 1833, Jacob Steiner gave a complete and systematic treatment of Poncelet's theorem. It is our aim in this section to develop a proof of the above Poncelet–Steiner theorem.

4.4.1 *Problem. Given points* A, B, U, P, *where* U *is the midpoint of* AB *and* P *is not on line* AB, *construct, with a straightedge alone, the line through* P *parallel to line* AB.

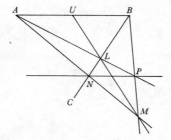

FIG. 4.4a

Draw (see Fig. 4.4a) lines AP, BP, and an arbitrary line BC through B cutting AP in L. Draw UL to cut BP in M. Draw AM to cut BC in N. Then PN is the sought parallel. The proof follows from the fact that in the complete quadrangle $ABPN$, PN must cut AB in the harmonic conjugate of U for A and B; since U is the midpoint of AB, the harmonic conjugate is the point at infinity on AB.

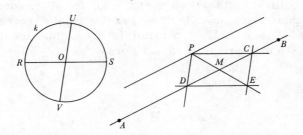

FIG. 4.4b

4.4.2 *Problem. Given a circle* k *with its center* O, *a line* AB, *and a point* P *not on* AB, *construct, with straightedge alone, the line through* P *parallel to line* AB.

Referring to Fig. 4.4b, draw any two diameters RS, UV of k not parallel to AB. Draw (by Problem 4.4.1) PC parallel to RS to cut AB in C, PD parallel to UV to cut AB in D, DE and CE parallel to RS and UV, respectively, to cut in E. Let PE cut DC in M. We now have a bisected segment on line AB and we may proceed as in Problem 4.4.1.

4.4.3 *Problem. Given a circle* k *with its center* O, *a line* AB, *and a point* P *not on* AB, *construct, with straightedge alone, the reflection of* P *in* AB.

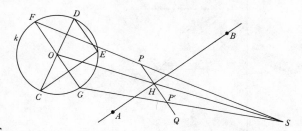

FIG. 4.4c

Referring to Fig. 4.4c, draw any diameter CD of k not parallel to AB. Draw (by Problem 4.4.2) chord CE parallel to AB, and then diameter FOG and line PQ parallel to DE. Let PQ cut AB in H and let FP and OH meet in S. Then GS cuts PQ in the sought point P'. If FP and OH are parallel, draw GS through G parallel to FP to cut PQ in the sought point P'. In either case, the proof follows from the fact that PHP' is homothetic to FOG.

If PQ collines with FG (see Fig. 4.4d) the above construction fails. In this case connect F, O, G with any point S' not on FG and cut these joins by a line parallel to FOG, obtaining the points F', O', G'. We may now proceed as before.

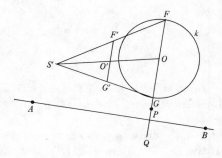

FIG. 4.4d

4.4.4 *Problem. Given a circle* k *with its center* O, *and points* A, B, C, D, *construct, with straightedge alone, the points of intersection of line* AB *and circle* C(D).

Referring to Fig. 4.4e, draw radius OR parallel to CD and let OC, RD meet in S. Draw any line DL and then RM parallel to DL

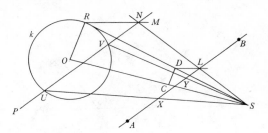

FIG. 4.4e

to cut SL in N. Draw NP parallel to AB to cut k in U and V. Now draw US, VS to cut AB in the sought points X and Y.

If O, D, C colline, find (by Problem 4.4.3) the reflection D' of D in any line through C, and proceed as before.

If $CD = OR$, then S is at infinity, but a construction can be carried out similar to the above by means of parallels.

If $C = O$, take $S = O$ (see Fig. 4.4f).

In all cases, a proof is easy by simple homothety considerations.

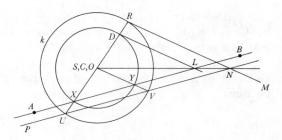

FIG. 4.4f

4.4.5   *Problem.   Given a circle* k *with its center* O, *and points* A, B, C, D, *construct, with straightedge alone, the radical axis of circles* A(B) *and* C(D).

Referring to Fig. 4.4g, draw $\overline{AQ}$ parallel to $\overline{CD}$. Find (by Problem 4.4.4) the point P where AQ cuts $A(B)$. AC and PD determine the external center of similitude S of $A(B)$ and $C(D)$. Draw any two lines through S to cut the circles in E, F, G, H and J, K, L, M, which can be found by Problem 4.4.4. Let JF and MG intersect in R and EK and HL in T. Then RT is the sought radical axis.

A proof may be given as follows. Since arcs FK and HM have the

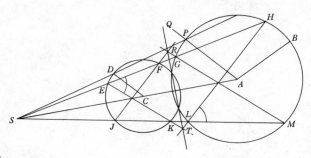

FIG. 4.4g

same angular measure, $\measuredangle\ HEK = \measuredangle\ HLM$. Therefore $HEKL$ is
concyclic, whence $(TK)(TE) = (TL)(TH)$, and T is on the radical
axis of $A(B)$ and $C(D)$. R is similarly on the radical axis of $A(B)$
and $C(D)$.

4.4.6 *Problem.   Given a circle* k *with its center* O, *and points* A, B,
C, D, *construct, with straightedge alone, the points of intersection of circles*
A(B) *and* C(D).

Find, by Problem 4.4.5, the radical axis of $A(B)$ and $C(D)$. Then,
by Problem 4.4.4, find the points of intersection of this radical
axis with $A(B)$.

4.4.7 *The Poncelet–Steiner Construction Theorem.   Any Euclidean
construction, insofar as the given and required elements are points, may be
accomplished with straightedge alone in the presence of a given circle and
its center.*

We leave the proof, which can be patterned after that of Theorem
4.3.3, to the reader.

PROBLEMS

4.4-1 It has recently been shown[†] that the Georg Mohr mentioned in Sec. 4.3 was the author of an anonymously published
booklet entitled *Compendium Euclidis Curiosi,* which appeared in
1673 and which in effect shows that all the constructions of
Euclid's *Elements* are possible with a straightedge and a given
rusty compass. Solve, with a straightedge and a given rusty
compass, the following first fourteen constructions found in
Mohr's work (see the second reference in the footnote).

---

†See A.E. Hallerberg, "The geometry of the fixed-compass," *The Mathematics Teacher*, Apr. 1959,
pp. 230–244, and A.E. Hallerberg, "Georg Mohr and Euclidis Curiosi," *The Mathematics Teacher*,
Feb. 1960, pp. 127–132.

(1)   To divide a given line into two equal parts.

(2)   To erect a perpendicular to a line from a given point in the given line.

(3)   To construct an equilateral triangle on a given side.

(4)   To erect a perpendicular to a line from a given point off the given line.

(5)   Through a given point to draw a line parallel to a given line.

(6)   To add two given line segments.

(7)   To subtract a shorter segment from a given segment.

(8)   Upon the end of a given line to place a given segment perpendicularly.

(9)   To divide a line into any number of equal parts.

(10)   Given two lines, to find the third proportional.

(11)   Given three lines, to find the fourth proportional.

(12)   To find the mean proportional to two given segments.

(13)   To change a given rectangle into a square.

(14)   To draw a triangle, given the three sides.

4.4-2   With a straightedge alone find the polar p of a given point P for a given circle k.

4.4-3   (a)   With a straightedge alone construct the tangents to a given circle k from a given external point P.

(b)   With a straightedge alone construct the tangent to a given circle k at a given point P on k.

4.4-4   Given three collinear points A, B, C with $AB = BC$, construct, with a straightedge alone, (a) the point X on line AB such that $AX = n(AB)$, where n is a given positive integer, (b) the point Y on AB such that $AY = (AB)/n$.

4.4-5   Supply the proof of Theorem 4.4.7.

4.5   IMPOSSIBILITY OF SOLVING THE THREE FAMOUS PROBLEMS WITH EUCLIDEAN TOOLS

It was not until the nineteenth century that the three famous problems of antiquity — that is, the duplication of the cube, the trisection of a general angle, and the quadrature of a circle — were finally shown to be impossible with Euclidean tools. The needed criteria for determining whether a given construction is or is not within the power of the tools turned out to be essentially algebraic in nature. In particular, the following two theorems (which we shall here accept without proof) were established. ‡

4.5.1   *Theorem.   From a given unit length it is impossible to construct with Euclidean tools a segment the magnitude of whose length is a root of a cubic equation with rational coefficients but with no rational root.*

4.5.2   *Theorem.   The magnitude of any length constructible with Euclidean tools from a given unit length is an algebraic number.* §

With the aid of the above two theorems we will dispose of the three famous problems of antiquity.

4.5.3   *Theorem.   The problem of duplicating a cube – that is, of constructing the edge of a cube having twice the volume of a given cube – is impossible with Euclidean tools.*

Let us take as our unit of length the edge of the given cube and let x denote the edge of the sought cube. Then we have $x^3 = 2$, or $x^3 - 2 = 0$. It follows that if a cube can be duplicated with Euclidean tools, we can, with these tools, construct from a unit segment a segment of length x. But this is impossible, by Theorem 4.5.1, since the cubic equation $x^3 - 2 = 0$ has rational coefficients but no rational root. ‖

4.5.4   *Theorem.   The problem of trisecting a general angle is impossible with Euclidean tools.*

We may prove that the *general* angle cannot be trisected with Euclidean tools by showing that some *particular* angle cannot be so trisected. Now, from trigonometry, we have the identity

$$\cos \theta = 4 \cos^3 (\theta/3) - 3 \cos (\theta/3).$$

Taking $\theta = 60°$ and setting $x = \cos (\theta/3)$ this becomes

$$8x^3 - 6x - 1 = 0.$$

Let OA (see Fig. 4.5a) be a given unit segment. Describe the circle $O(A)$ and then the circle $A(O)$ to intersect in B. Then ⊰ BOA = 60°. Let trisector OC, which makes ⊰ $COA = 20°$, cut the circle in C, and let D be the foot of the perpendicular from C

---

‡ See, e.g., Howard Eves, *A Survey of Geometry,* Vol. 2 (Boston: Allyn and Bacon, Inc., 1965), pp. 30–35.

§A number is said to be *algebraic* if it is a root of a polynomial equation having rational coefficients.

‖ It will be recalled that if a polynomial equation $a_0 x^n + a_1 x^{n-1} + \cdots + a_n = 0$, with integral coefficients $a_0, a_1, \cdots, a_n$, has a reduced rational root a/b, then a is a factor of a_n and b is a factor of a_0. Thus any rational roots of $x^3 - 2 = 0$ are among 1, -1, 2, -2. Since by direct testing none of these numbers satisfies the equation, the equation has no rational roots.

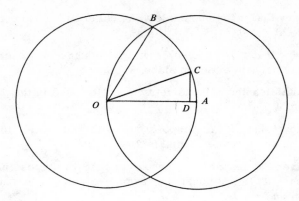

FIG. 4.5a

on OA. Then $OD = \cos 20° = x$. It follows that if a $60°$ angle can be trisected with Euclidean tools, in other words if OC can be drawn with these tools, we can construct from a unit segment OA another segment of length x. But this is impossible, by Theorem 4.5.1, since the above cubic equation has rational coefficients but no rational root.

It should be noted that we have not proved that *no* angle can be trisected with Euclidean tools, but only that *not all* angles can be so trisected. The truth of the matter is that $90°$ and an infinite number of other angles can be trisected by the use of Euclidean tools.

4.5.5 *Theorem.   The problem of squaring a circle – that is, of constructing a square whose area is equal to that of a given circle – is impossible with Euclidean tools.*

Let us take as our unit of length the radius of the given circle and let x denote the side of the sought square. Then we have $x = \sqrt{\pi}$. It follows that if we can square a circle with Euclidean tools, we can, with these tools, construct from a unit segment a segment of length $\sqrt{\pi}$. But this is impossible, by Theorem 4.5.2, since π, and hence also $\sqrt{\pi}$, was shown by Lindemann in 1882 to be non-algebraic.

PROBLEMS

4.5-1 Show that it is impossible with Euclidean tools to construct a regular polygon of nine sides.

4.5-2   Show that it is impossible with Euclidean tools to construct an angle of 1°.

4.5-3   Show that it is impossible with Euclidean tools to construct a regular polygon of seven sides.

4.5-4   Establish the trigonometric identity used in the proof of Theorem 4.5.4.

4.5-5   Show that it is impossible with Euclidean tools to trisect an angle whose cosine is 2/3.

4.5-6   Given a segment s, show that it is impossible with Euclidean tools to construct segments m and n such that $s : m = m : n = n : 2s$.

4.5-7   Show that it is impossible with Euclidean tools to construct a line segment whose length equals the circumference of a given circle.

4.5-8   Let $OADB$ be an arbitrary given rectangle. Show that it is impossible with Euclidean tools to draw a circle, concentric with the rectangle, cutting OA and OB produced in A' and B' such that A', D, B' are collinear.

4.5-9   Let AB be a given segment. Draw $\measuredangle ABM = 90°$ and $\measuredangle ABN = 120°$, both angles lying on the same side of AB. Show that it is impossible with Euclidean tools to draw a line ACD cutting BM in C and BN in D and such that $CD = AB$.

4.5-10   Let AOB be a central angle in a given circle. Show that it is impossible with Euclidean tools to draw a line BCD through B cutting the circle again in C, AO produced in D, and such that $CD = OA$.

4.5-11   Let us be given an angle AOB and a point P within the angle. The line through P cutting OA and OB in C and D so that $CE = PD$, where E is the foot of the perpendicular from O on CD, is known as *Philon's line for angle* AOB *and the point* P. It can be shown that Philon's line is the minimum chord CD that can be drawn through P. Show that in general it is impossible to construct with Euclidean tools Philon's line for a given angle and a given point.

V. PROJECTIVE GEOMETRY

Consider for a moment the problem an artist faces in attempting to paint a true picture of some object. As the artist looks at the object, rays of light from the object enter his eye. If a transparent screen should be placed between the artist's eye and the object, these rays of light would intersect the screen in a collection of points. It is this collection of points, which may be called the *image,* or *projection,* of the object on the screen, that the artist must draw on his paper or canvas if a viewer of the picture is to receive the same impression of the form of the object as he would receive were he to view the object itself. Since the artist's paper or canvas is not a transparent screen, the task of accurately drawing the desired projection presents a real problem to the artist. In an effort to produce more realistic pictures, many of the Renaissance artists and architects became deeply interested in discovering the formal laws controlling the construction of the projections of objects on a screen, and, in the fifteenth century, a number of these men created the elements of an underlying geometrical theory of perspective.

The theory of perspective was considerably extended in the early seventeenth century by a small group of French mathematicians, the motivator of whom was Gérard Desargues, an engineer and architect who was born in Lyons in 1593 and who died in the same city about 1662. Influenced by the growing needs of artists and architects for a deeper theory of perspective, Desargues published, in Paris in 1639, a remarkably original treatise on the

conic sections which exploited the idea of projection. But this
work was so neglected by most other mathematicians of the time
that it was soon forgotten and all copies of the publication disappeared. Two centuries later, when the French geometer Michel
Chasles (1793 - 1880) wrote a history of geometry, there was no
way to estimate the value of Desargues' work. Six years later,
however, in 1845, Chasles happened upon a manuscript copy of
Desargues' treatise, made by one of Desargues' few followers,
and since that time the work has been recognized as one of the
classics in the early development of projective geometry.

There are several reasons for the initial neglect of Desargues'
little volume. It was overshadowed by the more supple analytic
geometry introduced by Descartes two years earlier. Geometers
were generally either developing this new powerful tool or trying
to apply infinitesimals to geometry. Also, Desargues unfortunately
adopted a style and a terminology that were so eccentric that they
beclouded his work and discouraged others from attempting properly
to evaluate his accomplishments.

The reintroduction of projective considerations into geometry did
not occur until the late eighteenth century, when the great French
geometer Gaspard Monge (1746 - 1818) created his descriptive
geometry. This subject, which concerns a way of representing
and analyzing three dimensional objects by means of their projections on certain planes, had its origin in the design of fortifica-
tions. Monge was a very inspiring teacher, and there gathered
about him a group of brilliant students of geometry, among whom
were L. N. Carnot (1753 - 1823), Charles J. Brianchon (1785 -
1864), and Jean-Victor Poncelet (1788 - 1867).

The real revival of projective geometry was launched by Poncelet.
As a Russian prisoner of war, taken during Napoleon's retreat
from Moscow, and with no books at hand, Poncelet planned his
great work on projective geometry, which, after his release and
return to France, he published in Paris in 1822.* This work gave
tremendous impetus to the study of the subject and inaugurated the
so-called "great period" in the history of projective geometry.
There followed into the field a host of mathematicians, among
whom were Gergonne, Brianchon, Chasles, Plücker, Steiner,
Staudt, Reye, and Cremona—great names in the history of geometry,
and in the history of projective geometry in particular.

The work of Desargues and of Poncelet, and their followers, led
geometers to classify geometric properties into two categories, the

metric properties, in which the measure of distances and of angles intervenes, and the *descriptive properties,* in which only the positional connection of the geometric elements with respect to one another is concerned. The Pythagorean Theorem, that *the square on the hypotenuse of a right triangle is equal to the sum of the squares on the two legs,* is a metric property. As an example of a descriptive property we might mention the remarkable "mystic-hexagram" theorem of Blaise Pascal, which we have earlier considered for the case of a circle and which was inspired by the work of Desargues: *If a hexagon be inscribed in a conic, then the points of intersection of the three pairs of opposite sides are collinear, and, conversely, if the points of intersection of the three pairs of opposite sides of a hexagon are collinear, then the hexagon is inscribed in a conic.*

The distinction between the two types of geometric properties, at least in the case of plane figures, becomes clearer when viewed from the fact that the descriptive properties are unaltered when the figure is subjected to a projection, whereas the metric properties may no longer hold when the figure is projected. Thus, under a projection from one plane to another, a right triangle does not necessarily remain a right triangle, and so the Pythagorean relation does not necessarily hold for the projected figure; the Pythogorean Theorem is a metric theorem. In the case of Pascal's Theorem, however, a hexagon inscribed in a conic projects into a hexagon inscribed in a conic and collinear points project into collinear points, and hence the theorem is preserved; Pascal's Theorem is a descriptive theorem.

Many descriptive properties present themselves in the seeming form of metric properties. For example we have seen (in Theorem 2.4.7) that the cross ratio (AB,CD) of four points A, B, C, D on a straight line is unaltered when the line containing the four points is projected into another line and the four points A', B', C', D'. In other words, though the lengths of the various corresponding segments on the two lines are not necessarily equal to one another, nevertheless the two compound ratios

$$(\overline{A'C'}/\overline{C'B'})/(\overline{A'D'}/\overline{D'B'}) \quad \text{and} \quad (\overline{AC}/\overline{CB})/(\overline{AD}/\overline{DB}),$$

that is, the two cross ratios (AB,CD) and $(A'B',C'D')$, are equal in value, and thus the cross ratio of four collinear points is a descriptive property of those points.

The study of the descriptive properties of geometric figures is known as *projective geometry.*

Projective geometry has grown into a vast and singularly beautifully developed branch of geometry, and has become basic for many

geometrical studies. Some of its more elementary aspects will be
examined in this chapter.

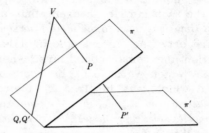

FIG. 5.1a

5.1   PERSPECTIVITIES AND PROJECTIVITIES

Let π and π' (see Fig. 5.1a) be two given fixed nonideal planes of
extended space, and let V be a given fixed point not lying on either
π or π'. Since the space is extended, π and π' are extended planes,
and point V may be either an ordinary or an ideal point. Let P
be any point, ordinary or ideal, of plane π. Then line VP will
intersect plane π' in a unique ordinary or ideal point P' of π'. In
this way the extended plane π is mapped onto the extended plane
π'. Indeed, since distinct points of π have distinct images in π',
the mapping is actually a transformation of the set of all points of
the extended plane π onto the set of all points of the extended
plane π'. The points on the line of intersection of planes π and
π' are invariant points of the transformation.

5.1.1   *Definitions.*   A transformation such as described above
is called a *perspectivity*, or a *perspective transformation*, and the
point V is called the *center* of the perspectivity. If V is an ordinary
point of space, the perspectivity is called a *central perspectivity*; if
V is an ideal point of space, the perspectivity is called a *parallel
perspectivity*. The line of intersection of π and π' is called the
axis of perspectivity. The line in π (π') which maps into the line at
infinity in π' (π) is called the *vanishing line* of π (π'). The point in
which a line of π (π') meets the vanishing line of π (π') is called
the *vanishing point* of the line.

A perspectivity or a product of two or more perspectivities is
called a *projectivity*, or a *projective transformation*. For example, a
perspectivity of center V of plane π onto plane π', followed by a
perspectivity of center W of plane π' onto plane π'', is a projectivity
of plane π onto plane π''.

It is clear that the two planes π and π' of a perspectivity must be taken as *extended* planes, since otherwise the correspondence between the points of the two planes might not be one-to-one. It is for this reason that an extended plane is often called a *projective plane*.

It is easily seen that a projectivity carries a straight line into a straight line. Very useful is the following special situation.

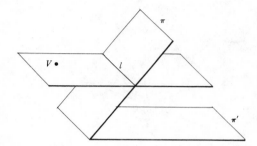

FIG. 5.1b

5.1.2   *Theorem.   If π is a given plane, 1 a given line in π, and V a given point not on π, then there exists a plane π' such that the perspectivity of center V carries line 1 of π into the line at infinity of π'.*

Choose for π' (see Fig. 5.1b) any plane parallel to (but not coincident with) the plane determined by V and l. Then it is clear that the line joining V to any point P on l will be parallel to plane π', that is, will meet π' at infinity.

5.1.3   *Definition.* The operation of selecting a suitable center of perspectivity V and a plane π' so that a given line l of a given plane π shall be mapped into the line at infinity of π' is called *projecting the given line to infinity.*

The operation of projecting a given line to infinity can often greatly simplify the proof of a theorem. We give some examples; the reader should note the application of the *transform-solve-invert* procedure. We first establish one of the harmonic properties of a complete quadrangle.

5.1.4   *Theorem.   Let* PQRS (see Fig. $5.1c_1$) *be a complete quadrangle and let* PQ *and* SR *intersect in* A, PR *and* SQ *intersect in* B, PS *and* QR *intersect in* C, AB *and* PS *intersect in* D. *Then* (PS,DC) = − 1.

Project line AC to infinity. Then $P'Q'R'S'$ (see Fig. $5.1c_2$) is a parallelogram and D' is the midpoint of $P'S'$. Since C' is at infinity, we have $(P'S', D'C') = -1$. The theorem now follows.

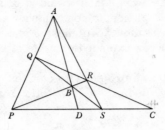

FIG. 5.1c₁

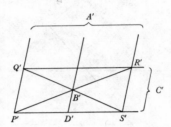

FIG. 5.1c₂

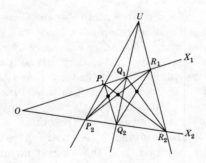

FIG. 5.1d₁

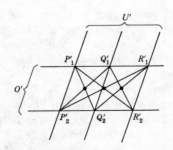

FIG. 5.1d₂

5.1.5   *Theorem.   If   the   three   lines* UP_1P_2, UQ_1Q_2, UR_1R_2 (see Fig. 5.1d_1) *intersect the two lines* OX_1 *and* OX_2 *in* P_1, Q_1, R_1 *and* P_2, Q_2, R_2, *respectively, then the points of intersection of* Q_1R_2 *and* Q_2R_1, R_1P_2 *and* R_2P_1, P_1Q_2 *and* P_2Q_1 *are collinear on a line that passes through point* O.

Project line *OU* to infinity. The projected figure appears as in Fig. 5.1d_2, where $P'_1P'_2$, $Q'_1Q'_2$, $R'_1R'_2$ are all parallel, and $P'_1Q'_1R'_1$ and $P'_2Q'_2R'_2$ are parallel. It is clear that the points of intersection of $Q'_1R'_2$ and $Q'_2R'_1$, $R'_1P'_2$ and $R'_2P'_1$, $P'_1Q'_2$ and $P'_2Q'_1$ are collinear on a line parallel to lines $P'_1Q'_1R'_1$ and $P'_2Q'_2R'_2$ (they lie on the line midway between lines $P'_1Q'_1R'_1$ and $P'_2Q'_2R'_2$). It follows that the corresponding points in the original figure are collinear on a line passing through point O.

5.1.6   *Desargues' Two–Triangle Theorem.   Copolar triangles in a plane are coaxial, and conversely.*

Let the two triangles (see Fig. 5.1e) be $A_1B_1C_1$ and $A_2B_2C_2$, and let B_1C_1 and B_2C_2 intersect in L, C_1A_1 and C_2A_2 intersect in M, A_1B_1 and A_2B_2 intersect in N.

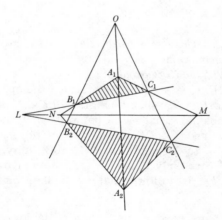

FIG. 5.1e

Suppose that A_1A_2, B_1B_2, C_1C_2 are concurrent in a point O. Project line *MN* to infinity. Then $A'_1B'_1$ and $A'_2B'_2$ are parallel, and $A'_1C'_1$ and $A'_2C'_2$ are parallel. It follows that $O'B'_1/O'B'_2 = O'A'_1/O'A'_2 = O'C'_1/O'C'_2$, whence $B'_1C'_1$ and $B'_2C'_2$ are also parallel. That is, the intersections of corresponding sides of triangles $A'_1B'_1C'_1$ and $A'_2B'_2C'_2$ are collinear (on the line at infinity). It follows that the intersections of corresponding sides of triangles $A_1B_1C_1$ and $A_2B_2C_2$ are collinear. That is, copolar triangles in a plane are coaxial.

Now suppose that L, M, N are collinear. Project line LMN to infinity. Then the two triangles $A'_1B'_1C'_1$ and $A'_2B'_2C'_2$ have their corresponding sides parallel, and hence are homothetic to one another, whence $A'_1A'_2, B'_1B'_2, C'_1C'_2$ are concurrent in a point O'. It follows that A_1A_2, B_1B_2, C_1C_2 are concurrent in a point O. That is, coaxial triangles in a plane are copolar.

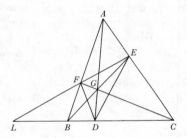

FIG. 5.1f

5.1.7   *Theorem.   There is a perspectivity that carries a given triangle* ABC *and a given point* G *in its plane (but not on a side line of the triangle) into a triangle* A'B'C' *and its centroid* G'.

Let AG, BG, CG (see Fig. 5.1f) intersect the opposite sides BC, CA, AB in points D, E, F. Then triangles DEF and ABC are copolar, and hence also coaxial. That is, the points L, M, N of intersection of EF and BC, FD and CA, DE and AB are collinear. By Theorem 5.1.4, $(BC,DL) = -1$. Project line LMN to infinity. Then D' is the midpoint of $B'C'$. Similarly E' and F' are the midpoints of $C'A'$ and $A'B'$ respectively. It follows that G' is the centroid of triangle $A'B'C'$.

If AD, BE, CF are concurrent cevian lines for a triangle ABC, Ceva's Theorem states that

$$\frac{(\overline{BD})(\overline{CE})(\overline{AF})}{(\overline{DC})(\overline{EA})(\overline{FB})} = +1.$$

The left member of this equation is a ratio of a product of some segments to a product of some other segments, and this ratio of products of segments has the two following interesting properties:

(1) If we replace $\overline{BD}$ by $B \times D$, and similarly treat all other segments appearing, and then regard the resulting expression as an algebraic one in the letters B, D, etc., these letters can all be canceled out.

(2) If we replace $\overline{BD}$ by a letter, say a, representing the line on which the segment is found, and similarly treat all other segments appearing, and then regard the resulting expression as an algebraic one in the letters a, etc., these letters can all be canceled out.

5.1.8 *Definition.* A ratio of a product of segments to another product of segments, where all the segments lie in one plane, is called by h-*expression* if it has the properties (1) and (2) described above.

5.1.9 *Theorem.* *The value of an h-expression is invariant under any projectivity.*

It is sufficient to show that a given h-expression has a value which is invariant under an arbitrary perspectivity. Let V be the center of a perspectivity and let $\overline{AB}$ be any one of the segments appearing in the h-expression. Let p denote the perpendicular distance from V to AB. Then

$$p\overline{AB} = (VA)(VB) \sin \overline{AVB},$$

since each side is twice the area of $\triangle \overline{VAB}$. It follows that

$$\overline{AB} = [(VA)(VB) \sin \overline{AVB}]/p.$$

Replace each segment $\overline{AB}$ in the h-expression by $[(VA)(VB) \sin \overline{AVB}]/p$. Since property (1) above holds, VA, VB, etc. cancel out; since property (2) above holds, p, etc. cancel out. We are left with an expression containing only the sines $\sin \overline{AVB}$, etc. Now, since $\angle \overline{AVB} = \angle \overline{A'VB'}$, etc., the same relation that holds among the sines $\sin \overline{AVB}$, etc. holds among the sines $\sin \overline{A'VB'}$, etc. Introducing factors VA', VB', p', etc., by reversing the earlier cancellations, leads to the same relation among segments $\overline{A'B'}$, etc. as was given among segments $\overline{AB}$, etc.

The reader will note that the procedure employed in the above proof is essentially the way we proved, in Sec. 2.4, that the cross ratio of four collinear points is invariant under a perspectivity.

5.1.10 *Ceva's Theorem.* *If* AD, BE, CF *are concurrent cevian lines for a triangle* ABC, *then*

$$\frac{(\overline{BD})(\overline{CE})(\overline{AF})}{(\overline{DC})(\overline{EA})(\overline{FB})} = +1. \tag{5.1}$$

The expression on the left of Eq. (5.1) is an h-expression, and is therefore (by Theorem 5.1.9) invariant in value under projection. By Theorem 5.1.7, there is a perspectivity which carries triangle ABC and the point G of concurrence of the three cevian lines into a triangle $A'B'C'$ and its centroid G'. Then $\overline{B'D'}/\overline{D'C'} = \overline{C'E'}/\overline{E'A'} = \overline{A'F'}/\overline{F'B'} = 1$, and clearly

$$\frac{(\overline{B'D'})(\overline{C'E'})(\overline{A'F'})}{(\overline{D'C'})(\overline{E'A'})(\overline{F'B'})} = +1.$$

The theorem now follows.

5.1.11 *Menelaus' Theorem. If* D, E, F *are collinear menelaus points on the sides* BC, CA, AB *of a triangle* ABC, *then*

$$\frac{(\overline{BD})(\overline{CE})(\overline{AF})}{(\overline{DC})(\overline{EA})(\overline{FB})} = -1. \tag{5.2}$$

The expression on the left of Eq. (5.2) is an h-expression, and is therefore (by Theorem 5.1.9) invariant in value under projection. Project line DEF to infinity. Then $\overline{B'D'}/\overline{D'C'} = \overline{C'E'}/\overline{E'A'} = \overline{A'F'}/\overline{F'B'} = -1$, and clearly

$$\frac{(\overline{B'D'})(\overline{C'E'})(\overline{A'F'})}{(\overline{D'C'})(\overline{E'A'})(\overline{F'B'})} = -1.$$

The theorem now follows.

We conclude the section by giving a proof of a theorem due to Pappus. This theorem is a generalization of Theorem 5.1.5, and is an instance of a descriptive theorem that was known to the ancient Greeks.

5.1.12 *Pappus' Theorem. If the vertices* 1, 2, 3, 4, 5, 6 *of a hexagon* 123456 *lie alternately on a pair of lines, then the three intersections* P,Q,R *of the opposite sides* 23 *and* 56, 45 *and* 12, 61 *and* 34 *of the hexagon are collinear* (see Fig. $5.1g_1$).

Project line PQ to infinity and suppose that the intersection O of

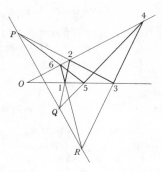

FIG. 5.1g₁

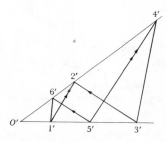

FIG. 5.1g₂

lines 135 and 246 does not lie on PQ. Then $1', 3', 5'$ are collinear, $2', 4', 6'$ are collinear, O' is a finite point, $2'3'$ is parallel to $5'6'$, and $4'5'$ is parallel to $1'2'$. We must prove that $6'1'$ is parallel to $3'4'$. Now (see Fig. 5.1g₂) since $2'3'$ is parallel to $5'6'$ and $4'5'$ is parallel to $1'2'$,

$$\overline{O'6'}/\overline{O'2'} = \overline{O'5'}/\overline{O'3'} \text{ and } \overline{O'1'}/\overline{O'5'} = \overline{O'2'}/\overline{O'4'}.$$

It follows that $\overline{O'6'}/\overline{O'1'} = \overline{O'4'}/\overline{O'3'}$ and $\overline{6'1'}$ is parallel to $\overline{3'4'}$.

If O lies on PQ, then lines $1'3'5'$ and $2'4'6'$ are parallel. But then $\overline{1'5'} = \overline{2'4'}$ and $\overline{5'3'} = \overline{6'2'}$. It follows that $\overline{1'3'} = \overline{6'4'}$ and $6'1'$ is parallel to $3'4'$.

PROBLEMS

5.1-1 (a) Prove that a projectivity carries a straight line into a straight line.

(b)   Prove that under a perspectivity a straight line and its image intersect each other on the axis of perspectivity.

6.1-2   (a)   Prove that under a perspectivity the angle between the images m' and n' of any two lines m and n is equal to the angle which the vanishing points of m and n subtend at the center V of perspectivity.

(b)   Prove that under a perspectivity all angles whose sides have the same vanishing points map into equal angles.

5.1-3   (a)   Given a plane π containing a line l and two angles ABC and DEF, where A, C, D, F are on l in the order A, D, C, F. Show that there exists a perspectivity which projects l to infinity and angles ABC and DEF into angles of given sizes α and β, respectively.

(b)   Must the segments AC and DF in part (a) separate each other?

5.1-4   Show that there exists a perspectivity which projects a given quadrilateral $ABCD$ into a square.

5.1-5   Prove that the cross ratio of a pencil of four distinct coplanar lines is preserved by projection.

5.1-6   Show that in a perspectivity carrying a plane π into a nonparallel plane π' there are in each plane exactly two points such that every angle at either of them projects into an equal angle. (These points are called the *isocenters* of the perspectivity.)

5.1-7   Show that in a perspectivity carrying a plane π into a nonparallel plane π' there is in each plane, besides the axis of perspectivity, a line whose segments are projected into equal segments. (These lines are called the *isolines* of the perspectivity.)

5.1-8   Lines VAA', VBB', VCC' cut two lines OX, OY in A and A', B and B', C and C' respectively. AB' and $A'C$ intersect in P; $A'B$ and AC' intersect in Q. Prove that line PQ passes through V.

5.1-9   If P, Q, R are any three points on the sides BC, CA, AB respectively of a triangle ABC, show that $(\overline{BP}/\overline{PC})(\overline{CQ}/\overline{QA})(\overline{AR}/\overline{RB})$ is invariant in value under projection.

5.1-10   In the complete quadrangle $ABCD$, a transversal cuts sides AB and CD in M and M', sides BC and AD in N and

N', and sides AC and BD in P and P'. Show that

$$(\overline{MN})(\overline{MN'})/(\overline{MP})(\overline{MP'}) = (\overline{M'N})(\overline{M'N'})/(\overline{M'P})(\overline{M'P'}).$$

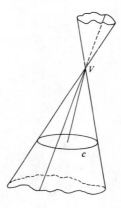

FIG. 5.2a

5.2   PROPER CONICS

We commence by informally stating a number of definitions which are very likely already familiar to the reader.

A *circular cone* (see Fig. 5.2a) is a surface generated by a straight line which moves so that it always intersects a given circle c and passes through a fixed point V not in the plane of the circle. The generating line, in each of its positions, is called an *element* of the cone; the fixed point is called the *vertex* of the cone. The vertex divides each element into two half-lines and divides the cone into two *nappes*, each of which is generated by one of the half-lines. If the line joining the vertex of the cone to the center of the given circle is perpendicular to the plane of the circle, the cone is called a *right circular cone*; otherwise it is called an *oblique circular cone*.

The curves called parabolas, ellipses, and hyperbolas were named by Apollonius, and were investigated by him as certain planar sections of right and oblique circular cones. Since these curves are intersections of circular cones by planes, they are examples of *conic sections*, or more briefly, *conics*. If the cutting plane does not pass through the vertex of the cone, the conic is called a *proper* conic. A *parabola* is a proper conic whose plane of section is parallel to one and only one element of the cone; an *ellipse* (including a circle as a special case) is a proper conic whose plane of section cuts all the elements of one nappe of the cone; a *hyperbola* is a proper conic whose plane of section cuts into both nappes of the cone. Figure 5.2b shows a right circular cone sectioned to yield a parabola *p*, an ellipse *e*, and a hyperbola *h*.

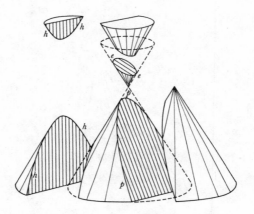

FIG. 5.2b

In ordinary space, a parabola is clearly a one-piece nonclosed curve; an ellipse is a one-piece closed curve; a hyperbola is a two-piece nonclosed curve. In extended space, each curve is one-piece and closed.

Since a proper conic is a section of a circular cone, and the section does not pass through the vertex of the cone, it follows that a proper conic is the image of a circle under a perspectivity. Therefore any property of a circle which is descriptive, that is, is unaltered by projection, can be transferred at once to the conic. In this way we obtain the following sequence of theorems about proper conics.

5.2.1   *Theorem.   A straight line in the plane of a proper conic cuts the conic in two points, is tangent to the conic, or fails to cut the conic.*

5.2.2   *Theorem.   There is a unique tangent line to a proper conic at each point on the conic.*

5.2.3   *Theorem.   A proper conic divides its plane, exclusive of the conic itself, into two regions such that from any point in one of the regions two lines can be drawn tangent to the conic, and from any point in the other region no line can be drawn tangent to the conic.*

5.2.4   *Definitions.*   The two regions mentioned in Theorem 5.2.3

are called, respectively, the *outside* and the *inside* of the proper conic.

5.2.5 *Theorem.* *If a variable line through a given point* P *in the plane of a proper conic* c *intersects the conic, the harmonic conjugates of the point with respect to the intersections of the line and conic all lie on a straight line* p. (See Corollary 3.8.8)

5.2.6 *Definitions.* The straight line *p* of Theorem 6.2.5 is called the *polar* of the point *P* for the conic *c*, and point *P* is called the *pole* of line *p* for the conic *c*.

5.2.7 *Theorem.* (1) *The polar of a point for a proper conic intersects the conic, is tangent to the conic at the point, or does not intersect the conic, according as the point is outside, on, or inside the conic.* (2) *If point* P *is outside a proper conic, then its polar for the conic passes through the points of contact of the tangents to the conic from* P. (See Theorem 3.8.2.)

5.2.8 *Theorem.* (1) *If, for a given proper conic, the polar of* P *passes through* Q, *then the polar of* Q *passes through* P. (2) *If, for a given proper conic, the pole of line* p *lies on line* q, *then the pole of* q *lies on* p. (3)*If, for a given proper conic,* P *and* Q *are the poles of* p *and* q, *then the pole of line* PQ *is the point of intersection of* p *and* q. (See Theorem 3.8.3.)

5.2.9 *Definitions.* Two points such that each lies on the polar of the other, for a given proper conic, are called *conjugate points* for the conic; two lines such that each passes through the pole of the other, for a given proper conic, are called *conjugate lines* for the conic.

5.2.10 *Theorem.* For a given proper conic: (1) *Each point of a line has a conjugate point on that line.* (2) *Each line through a point has a conjugate line through that point.* (3) *Of two distinct conjugate points on a line that cuts the conic, one is inside and the other outside the conic.* (4) *Of two distinct conjugate lines that intersect outside the conic, one cuts the conic and the other does not.* (5) *Any point on the conic is conjugate to all the points on the tangent to the conic at the point.* (6) *Any tangent to the conic is conjugate to all the lines through its point of contact with the conic.* (See Theorem 3.8.6.)

5.2.11 *Theorem.* *If, for a given proper conic, two conjugate points lie on a line which intersects the conic, they are harmonically separated by the points of intersection.* (See Theorem 3.8.7.)

5.2.12 *Theorem.* *If, for a given proper conic, two conjugate lines intersect outside the conic, they are harmonically separated by the tangents to the conic from their point of intersection.* (See Theorem 3.8.9.)

5.2.13 *Theorem.* *If A, B, C, D are four distinct collinear points, and* a, b, c, d *are their polars for a given proper conic, then* (AB,CD) = (ab,cd). (See Theorem 3.8.10.)

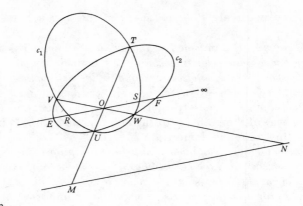

FIG. 5.2c

5.2.14   Theorem.   *If* ABCD *is a complete quadrangle inscribed in a proper conic, then each diagonal point of the quadrangle is the pole, for the conic, of the line determined by the other two diagonal points.* (See Theorem 3.8.12.)

5.2.15   The Generalized Butterfly Theorem.   *Let* O *(see Fig. 5.2c) be the midpoint of a given chord* RS *of a proper conic* c_1, *let two other chords* TU *and* VW *be drawn through* O, *and let a conic* c_2 *through* U, V, T, W *cut the given chord in* E *and* F. *Then* O *is the midpoint of* EF.

Let MN, the polar of O for conic c_1, cut TU in M and VW in N. Then, since $(VW,ON) = (TU,OM) = -1, MN$ is also the polar of O for conic c_2. Moreover, RS is parallel to MN since $(RS,O\infty) = -1$. Therefore $(EF,O\infty) = -1$ and O is the midpoint of EF. (See Theorem 3.8.13.)

5.2.16   Pascal's Theorem.   *If a hexagon (not necessarily convex) is inscribed in a proper conic, the three points of intersection of pairs of opposite sides of the hexagon are collinear.* (See Theorem 2.3.10.)

5.2.17   Brianchon's Theorem.   *If a hexagon (not necessarily convex) is circumscribed about a proper conic, the three lines joining pairs of opposite vertices of the hexagon are concurrent.* (See Theorem 3.8.11.)

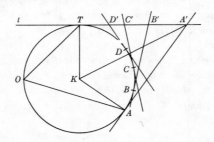

FIG. 5.2d

5.2.18   *Chasles' Theorem.   Let* A, B, C, D *be four distinct points on a proper conic and let the tangents to the conic at* A, B, C, D *meet a fixed tangent* t *to the conic in the points* A′, B′, C′, D′, *respectively. Then, if* O *is any point on the conic,* O(AB,CD) = (A′B′,C′D′).

Since the theorem is a projective one, it suffices to establish it for the case where the proper conic is a circle. Let K be the center of the circle (see Fig. 5.2d), and T the point of contact of the tangent t. Then $\angle A'KT = \frac{1}{2} \angle AKT = \angle AOT$. It follows that pencils $O(ABCD)$ and $K(A'B'C'D')$ are congruent, and $O(AB,CD) = K(A'B',C'D') = (A'B',C'D')$.

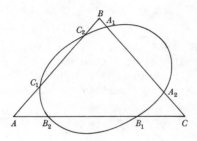

FIG. 5.2e

5.2.19   *Carnot's Theorem.   If* (see Fig. 5.2e) *the sides* BC, CA, AB *of a triangle* ABC *cut a proper conic in the points* A_1 *and* A_2, B_1 *and* B_2, C_1 *and* C_2, *respectively, then*

$$(\overline{AC_1})(\overline{AC_2})(\overline{BA_1})(\overline{BA_2})(\overline{CB_1})(\overline{CB_2}) =$$

$$(\overline{AB_1})(\overline{AB_2})(\overline{BC_1})(\overline{BC_2})(\overline{CA_1})(\overline{CA_2}). \quad (5.3)$$

We shall assume that no one of the points of the intersection is either an ideal point or a vertex of the triangle. Then the left member of Eq. (5.3) divided by the right member of Eq. (5.3) is an h-expression, and is therefore (by Theorem 5.1.9) invariant in value under projection. By the definition of a proper conic, there is a perspectivity which carries the conic into a circle. Now relation (5.3) holds for a circle, since $(\overline{A'C'_1})(\overline{A'C'_2}) = (\overline{A'B'_1})(\overline{A'B'_2})$, etc. Hence the h-expression has the value $+1$, and the theorem follows.

PROBLEMS

5.2-1   If PQ is a chord of a proper conic, U any point on line

PQ, and V the point where the polar of U for the conic cuts line PQ, show that $1/\overline{PV} + 1/\overline{QV} = $ constant.

5.2-2   Let A, B, C be three points on a proper conic, CT the tangent to the conic at C, and CD such that $C(TD,AB) = -1$. Show that CD passes through the pole of AB.

5.2-3   A chord PQ is drawn through the midpoint U of a chord AB of a proper conic. If the tangents at P and Q cut AB in L and M, prove that U is the midpoint of LM.

5.2-4 A, B, C, D are four points on a proper conic; AB and CD intersect in R; AC and BD intersect in S; the tangents to the conic at A and D intersect in T. Prove that R, S, T are collinear.

5.2-5   We define the *center* of a proper conic to be the pole for the conic of the line at infinity. Prove the following:
(a)   The center of a parabola is at infinity.
(b)   The center of a hyperbola is an ordinary point lying outside the curve.
(c)   The center of an ellipse is an ordinary point lying inside the curve.
Hyperbolas and ellipses are called *central conics*.
(d)   The center of a central conic bisects every chord of the conic through it, and is thus a center of symmetry of the conic.
(e)   All proper conics circumscribing a parallelogram have their centers at the center of the parallelogram.
(f)   If C is the center of a central conic, TP and TQ touch the conic at P and Q, and CT cuts PQ in V and the conic in U, then $(\overline{CV})(\overline{CT}) = (CU)^2$.

5.2-6   The locus of the midpoints of a family of parallel chords of a proper conic is called a *diameter* of the conic. Prove the following:
(a)   Diameters of a proper conic are straight lines.
(b)   All diameters of a central conic pass through the center.
(c)   All diameters of a parabola are parallel.
(d)   The tangents at the ends of a diameter of a central conic are parallel to the chords which the diameter bisects.
(e)   If the tangents at the ends of a chord of a central conic are parallel, the chord is a diameter of the conic.
(f)   Two chords of a central conic which bisect each other are diameters of the conic.

5.2-7   Two diameters of a central conic which are conjugate lines for the conic are called a pair of *conjugate diameters* of the conic. Prove the following:

(a)   Each of two conjugate diameters of a central conic bisects the chords parallel to the other.

(b)   The diagonals of a parallelogram circumscribing a central conic are conjugate diameters of the conic; the points of contact are the vertices of a parallelogram whose sides are parallel to the above diagonals.

(c)   If each diameter of a central conic is perpendicular to its conjugate diameter, the conic is a circle.

5.2-8   The tangents to a hyperbola from its center are called the *asymptotes* of the hyperbola. Prove the following:

(a)   The asymptotes of a hyperbola harmonically separate every pair of conjugate diameters of the hyperbola.

(b)   Let a line cut a hyperbola in Q and Q', and cut its asymptotes in R and R'. Then $RQ = Q'R'$.

(c)   The intercept between the asymptotes of a hyperbola on any tangent to the hyperbola is bisected by the point of contact of the tangent.

5.2-9   With straightedge alone: (a) Draw the tangents to a proper conic from a given point outside the conic. (b) Draw the tangent to a proper conic at a given point on the conic.

5.2-10   The sides $AB, BC, CD, \cdots$ of a polygon intersect a proper conic in A_1 and A_2, B_1 and B_2, C_1 and $C_2, \cdots$. Show that

$$(\overline{AA_1})(\overline{AA_2})(\overline{BB_1})(\overline{BB_2})(\overline{CC_1})(\overline{CC_2}) \cdots =$$

$$(\overline{BA_1})(\overline{BA_2})(\overline{CB_1})(\overline{CB_2})(\overline{DC_1})(\overline{DC_2}) \cdots .$$

(This is a generalization of Carnot's Theorem.)

5.2-11 B_1B_2 and A_1A_2 are two variable chords of a proper conic drawn through two fixed points A and B, respectively. If A_1A_2, B_1B_2 intersect in C, show that

$$(BA_1)(BA_2)(CB_1)(CB_2)/(AB_1)(AB_2)(CA_1)(CA_2)$$

is constant.

5.3   THE PRINCIPLE OF DUALITY

There is, in plane projective geometry, a remarkable symmetry between points and lines, such that if in a true projective proposition about "points" and "lines" we interchange these two words, and perhaps smooth out the language, we obtain another true projective proposition about "lines" and "points." The reader very likely has already noticed this symmetric pairing of the propositions of projective geometry. As a simple example, consider the following two propositions related in this way:

Any two distinct points determine one and only one line on which they both lie.

Any two distinct lines determine one and only one point through which they both pass.

In an ordinary plane, only the first of these two propositions is true without exception. In an extended, or projective, plane, however, both propositions are true without exception — regardless of whether the points and lines involved are ordinary or ideal.

We note that in passing from the statement of the first proposition to the statement of the second proposition, we not only interchanged the words "point" and "line," but we also altered the final phrase somewhat. Had we not altered the final phrase, the second proposition would have sounded a trifle awkward. This awkwardness of sound, however, results only because of a blemish in our language. Since the relation of a point P lying on a line l and that of a line l passing through a point P are symmetrical relations, a perfect language would express the two relations by a symmetrical terminology. We accordingly agree, in projective geometry, to express these two relations by the two phrases "point P is on line l" and "line l is on point P." Employing this modified language, we can pass directly from the statement of either of the propositions to that of the other by a mere mechanical interchange of the words "point" and "line."

For convenience, we call our modified language the *on–language*. The observed symmetry between points and lines in plane projective geometry leads to the so-called *principle of duality* for the plane, which may now be stated as follows:

5.3.1   *The Principle of Duality for the Plane. If in a true projective proposition, stated in the on–language, about points and lines in a plane, we interchange the words "point" and "line," we obtain a second true projective proposition, stated in the on–language, about lines and points in a plane.*

The principle of duality, which pairs the propositions of plane projective geometry, is of far-reaching consequence, and was first explicitly stated by Joseph–Diez Gergonne in 1826, though it was led up to by the works of Poncelet and others during the first quarter of the nineteenth century. Once the principle of duality is in some way established, then the proof of one proposition of a dual pair automatically carries with it the proof of the other.

Pascal's Theorem is a projective proposition; let us dualize it. We first note that a curve may be regarded either as the locus of its points or as the envelope of its tangents (see Fig. 5.3a).

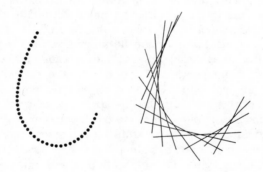

FIG. 5.3a

From the first point of view, the curve is called a *point curve*; from the second point of view, it is called a *line curve*. We now state Pascal's Theorem in the on–language as follows:

If the six points 1, 2, 3, 4, 5, 6 lie on a proper point conic, then the points determined by the three pairs of lines (12), (45); (23), (56); (34), (61) lie on a line.

Dualizing we obtain:

If the six lines 1, 2, 3, 4, 5, 6 lie on a proper line conic, then the lines determined by the three pairs of points (12), (45); (23), (56); (34), (61) lie on a point.

This dual is, of course, Brianchon's Theorem. Using less artificial language, Pascal's Theorem and its dual may now be stated as:

If a hexagon is inscribed in a proper conic, then the points of intersection of the three pairs of opposite sides are collinear.

If a hexagon is circumscribed about a proper conic, then the lines joining the three pairs of opposite vertices are concurrent.

With a little practice, one becomes adept at dualizing a proposition of projective geometry without having to resort to the artificial on-language.

Poncelet maintained that the principle of duality is a consequence of the theory of poles and polars, which, though known earlier, received its first systematic development in his hands. If Γ is a fixed proper conic, then to each point P of the extended plane can be associated the polar p' of P for the conic, and to each line l of the extended plane can be associated the pole L' of l for the conic. This correspondence, which maps the points and lines of the extended plane onto the lines and points of the extended plane, possesses some important properties. First of all, the correspondence is invariant under projection. Further, an incident point and line map into an incident line and point, collinear points map into concurrent lines, and concurrent lines map into collinear points.

Now imagine that we have established a projective property about a plane figure F composed of points and lines. Let F' be the figure which one obtains by replacing the points and lines of F by their polars and poles with respect to a given proper conic Γ lying in the plane of F. Then one will obtain from the projective property of figure F a corresponding projective property of figure F', in which the roles played by the words "point" and "line" have been interchanged. The two propositions will be the duals of each other.

There are today more satisfying ways of establishing the principle of duality of plane projective geometry.

PROBLEMS

5.3-1   Write a description of each of the figures 5.3b through 5.3i; dualize each description and sketch the dual figure.

5.3-2   What is the dual of a complete quadrangle?

5.3-3   State the dual of the following theorem: If points X, Y, U

are collinear and if $X(AB,CU) = Y(AB,CU)$, then points A, B, C are collinear.

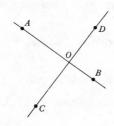

FIG. 5.3b

FIG. 5.3c

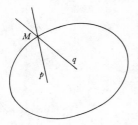

FIG. 5.3d

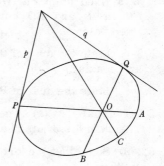

FIG. 5.3e

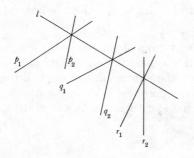

FIG. 5.3f

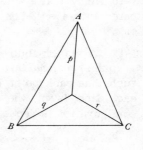

FIG. 5.3g

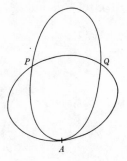

FIG. 5.3h

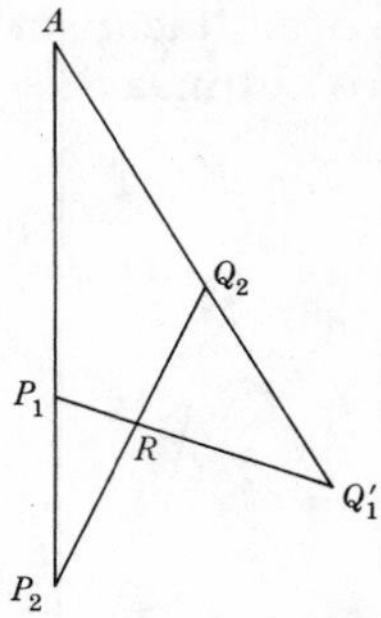

FIG. 5.3i

5.3-4 State the dual of the following theorem: ABC is a triangle, L a fixed point on AB, O a variable point on CL. If AO cuts CB in P and BO cuts CA in Q, then PQ intersects AB in a fixed point M.

5.3-5 State the dual of the following theorem: Copolar triangles are coaxial.

5.3-6 State the dual of Pappus' Theorem 5.1.13.

5.3-7 Dualize: (a) Theorem 5.2.1, (b) Theorem 5.2.5, (c) Theorem 5.2.8, (d) Theorem 5.2.14.

5.3-8 Show that Theorems 5.2.11 and 5.2.12 are duals of one another.

5.3-9 Prove that the reciprocal of a pole and polar for a proper conic is a polar and pole for the reciprocal conic.

5.3-10 Show that a self-conjugate triangle for a conic c reciprocates into a self-conjugate triangle for the reciprocal conic of c.

5.3-11 A planar figure consisting of points and lines is called a (plane) *configuration* if it consists of a_{11} points and a_{22} lines such that each point is on the same number (a_{12}) of lines and each line is on the same number (a_{21}) of points. A (plane) configuration is represented symbolically by the matrix

$$\begin{pmatrix} a_{11} & a_{12} \\ a_{21} & a_{22} \end{pmatrix}.$$

(a) Show that the dual of a configuration is a configuration, and give its matrix.
(b) Show that the figure of Desargues' Theorem in the plane is a self-dual configuration, and give its matrix.

5.4 THE FOCUS-DIRECTRIX PROPERTY

We have defined a proper conic as any section of a right or oblique circular cone made by a plane not passing through the vertex of the cone. It is a remarkable fact, which we do not establish here, that all proper conics can be obtained as sections of only *right* circular cones; indeed, they can all be obtained as sections of any one given right circular cone.

Using the above fact that a proper conic is always a section of a right circular cone, we now derive a basic property of these curves which is customarily employed when studying these curves by analytic geometry.

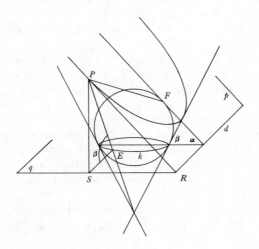

FIG. 5.4a

5.4.1 *Theorem. A noncircular proper conic is the locus of a point moving in a plane so that the ratio of its distance from a fixed point in the plane to its distance from a fixed line in the plane, not passing through the fixed point, is a constant.*

Consider the conic as a section made by a plane *p* cutting a right circular cone (see Fig. 5.4a). Let *s* be a sphere inside the cone, touching the cone along a circle k whose plane we shall call q, and also touching plane p at point F. Let planes p and q intersect in a line d. From P, any point on the conic section, drop a perpendicular PR onto line d and a perpendicular PS onto plane q. Let the element of the cone through P cut q in point E. Finally, let α be the angle between planes p and q, and β the angle an element of the cone makes with plane q. Then, since $PF = PE$ (the segments being tangent lines from an external point to a sphere), and triangles PSE and PSR are right triangles with right angles at S, we have

$$PF/PR = PE/PR = (PS/PR)/(PS/PE) = \sin \alpha \ / \ \sin \beta = e,$$

a constant independent of the position of P on the conic. The conic may therefore be considered as the curve generated by a point P moving in the plane p such that the ratio of its distance from the point F of p to its distance from the line d of p is a constant e.

    5.4.2 *Definitions.* The fixed point F of Theorem 5.4.1 is called a *focus* of the conic, the fixed line d is called a *directrix* of the conic, and the constant e is called the *eccentricity* of the conic.

    5.4.3 *Theorem. If e is the eccentricity of a proper conic, then the conic is a parabola, an ellipse, or a hyperbola according as $e = 1$, $e < 1$, or $e > 1$.*

    If plane p in Fig. 5.4a is parallel to one and only one element of the cone, then $\alpha = \beta$, and $e = 1$; if plane p cuts every element of one nappe of the cone, then $\alpha < \beta$, and $e < 1$; if p cuts both nappes of the cone, then $\alpha > \beta$, and $e > 1$.

    5.4.4 *Remark.* When plane p of Fig. 5.4a is parallel to plane q, the section is a circle. In this case there is no finite directrix d, but one easily sees that this situation can be considered as a limiting position obtained by letting the intersection d of planes p and q move farther and farther away from the cone, the angle α, and hence also the fraction $\sin \alpha \ / \sin \beta$, becoming closer and closer to 0. This state of affairs is described by saying that the directrix of a circle is at infinity and the eccentricity of a circle is 0.

    5.4.5 *Theorem. An ellipse is the locus of a point moving in a plane such that the sum of its distances from two fixed points in the plane is a constant.*

    Consider the ellipse as a section of a right circular cone (see Fig. 5.4b). Let s_1 and s_2 be two spheres touching the plane p of the ellipse at the points F_1 and F_2, respectively, and touching the cone along the parallel circles k_1 and k_2, respectively. Join an arbitrary point P of the ellipse to F_1 and F_2, and let the element of the cone through P cut k_1 and k_2 in E_1 and E_2, respectively. Then $PF_1 = PE_1$ and $PF_2 = PE_2$ (each pair of equal segments being tangent lines from an external point to a sphere). It follows that

$$PF_1 + PF_2 = PE_1 + PE_2 = E_1E_2,$$

a constant independent of the position of P on the ellipse.

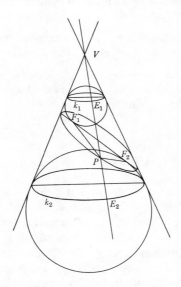

FIG. 5.4b

Note that if the ellipse is a circle, then F_1 and F_2 coincide at the center of the circle.

5.4.6   *Theorem.   A hyperbola is the locus of a point moving in a plane such that the difference of its distances from two fixed points in the plane is a constant.*

We leave the establishment of this theorem, along the lines of the proof of Theorem 5.4.5, to the reader.

The simple and elegant approach of this section was discovered around the first quarter-mark of the nineteenth century by the two Belgian geometers Adolphe Quetelet (1796 - 1874) and Germinal Dandelin (1794 - 1847).

PROBLEMS

5.4-1   Establish Theorem 5.4.6.

5.4-2   Show that hyperbolas and noncircular ellipses have two distinct foci and two associated directrices, each directrix being perpendicular to the line joining the two foci.

5.4-3   Show that there exists an ellipse for each positive eccentricity $e < 1$, and there exists a hyperbola for each eccentricity $e > 1$.

5.4-4   Show that there are two plane sections of a right circular cone which have a focus at a given point within the cone.

5.4-5   Prove that the sum of the distances of the vertex of a right circular cone from the ends of any diameter of a given elliptic section is constant.

5.5   ORTHOGONAL PROJECTION

Let π and π' be two planes not perpendicular to one another. The mapping of plane π onto plane π' which carries each point P of π into the foot P' of the perpendicular from P to π' is called the *orthogonal projection* of plane π onto plane π'.

Orthogonal projection, being a particular kind of perspectivity, has all the properties of a perspectivity, but it also has some special properties not possessed by all perspectivities. It is because of these special properties that orthogonal projection is such a highly useful transformation. We now establish some of the special properties.

5.5.1   *Theorem.   Under an orthogonal projection of a plane π onto a plane π' not perpendicular to π:*

(1) *ordinary points correspond to ordinary points,*

(2) *the lines at infinity correspond,*

(3) *parallel lines correspond to parallel lines,*

(4) *the ratio of two segments on a line is unaltered,*

(5) *the ratio of two segments on parallel lines is unaltered,*

(6) *the centroid of a triangle corresponds to the centroid of the corresponding triangle,*

(7) *if* A *and* A' *are two corresponding areas, then* A' = A cos θ, *where θ is the angle between planes π and π',*

(8) *the ratio of two areas is unaltered,*

(9) *circles map into homothetic ellipses.*

The first property is obvious and the next two are consequences of the first one. Properties (4) and (5) follow from the fact that the length of a line segment in π' is equal to the length of the corresponding segment in π multiplied by the cosine of the angle between the lines of the two segments. Property (6) is a consequence of property (4). Property (7) follows from the fact that any area in π can be considered as the limit of the sum of thin rectangular strips of common width parallel to the line of intersection of planes π and π', the limit being taken as the number of strips increases indefinitely; the lengths of these strips are unaltered by the projection, but their width w becomes $w \cos \theta$. Property (8) is a consequence of property (7). A circle clearly projects into an ellipse having its major axis parallel to the line of intersection of planes π and π'; also, if a and b are the semimajor and semiminor axes of the ellipse, and r is the radius of the circle, $a = r$ and $b = r \cos \theta$, and property (9) follows.

5.5.2 *Theorem. Any ellipse may be orthogonally projected into a circle.*

Let π be the plane of the ellipse and let a and b be the semimajor and semiminor axes of the ellipse. Through a line in π parallel to the minor axis of the ellipse, pass a plane π' making an angle $\theta = \cos^{-1} (b/a)$ with π. The reader may now easily show that the orthogonal projection of the ellipse to plane π' is a circle of radius b.

5.5.3 *Corollary. If an ellipse is orthogonally projected into a circle, then circles in the plane of projection correspond to those ellipses of the original plane which are homothetic to the given ellipse.*

5.5.4 *Theorem. Any triangle may be orthogonally projected into an equilateral triangle.*

Let the given triangle be ABC and let L, M, N be the midpoints of the sides BC, CA, AB, respectively. There is a proper conic, which in this case clearly must be an ellipse, tangent to BC, CA, AB at L, M, N. Orthogonally project this ellipse into a circle (by Theorem 5.5.2), triangle ABC and points L, M, N thereby mapping into triangle $A'B'C'$ and points L', M', N'. Then, since $B'L' = L'C' = C'M' = M'A' = A'N' = N'B'$, it follows that triangle $A'B'C'$ is equilateral.

We now give a few applications of orthogonal projection; further applications will be found in the problems at the end of the section.

The reader should note the employment of the *transform-solve-invert* procedure.

5.5.5 Theorem. A necessary and sufficient condition for a triangle inscribed in an ellipse to have maximum area is that the centroid of the triangle coincide with the center of the ellipse.

Orthogonally project the ellipse into a circle (Theorem 5.5.2). Triangles of maximum area in the ellipse correspond to triangles of maximum area in the circle (Theorem 5.5.1(8)). But a necessary and sufficient condition for a triangle inscribed in a circle to have maximum area is that the triangle be equilateral, and a necessary and sufficient condition for the triangle to be equilateral is that its centroid coincide with the center of the circle. The theorem now follows (Theorem 5.5.1(6) and Corollary 5.5.3).

5.5.6 Theorem. The envelope of a chord of an ellipse which cuts off a segment of constant area is a concentric homothetic ellipse.

Orthogonally project the ellipse into a circle (Theorem 5.5.2). The variable chord of the ellipse corresponds to a variable chord of the circle which cuts off a circular segment of constant area (Theorem 5.5.1(8)). But the envelope of the variable chord of the circle is a concentric circle. The theorem now follows (Corollary 5.5.3).

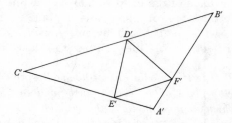

FIG. 5.5a

5.5.7 Theorem. The area of a triangle DEF inscribed in a given triangle ABC cannot be less than the area of each of the other three triangles formed.

Orthogonally project the inscribed triangle *DEF* into an equilateral triangle *D'E'F'* (see Fig. 5.5a). It suffices to prove the theorem for the projected figure (Theorem 5.5.1(8)). Now if triangle *A'B'C'* is equilateral, then clearly the area of no subtriangle can exceed that of *D'E'F'*. Otherwise there is some angle, say *A'*, greater than 60°. But then the perpendicular from *A'* on *E'F'* is less than the perpendicular from *D'* on *E'F'*, and the area of triangle *D'E'F'* is greater than the area of triangle *A'E'F'*.

The following theorem appeared as a problem on the 1958 Kürschák Prize Competition, an annual high school mathematics contest held in Hungary.

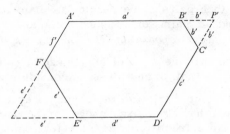

FIG. 5.5b

5.5.8 *Theorem. If in the convex hexagon* ABCDEF *every pair of opposite sides are parallel, then triangles* ACE *and* BDF *have equal areas.*

Let AB and DC intersect in P. Orthogonally project triangle BCP into an equilateral triangle $B'C'P'$ (see Fig. 5.5b). Then the given hexagon $ABCDEF$ projects into a hexagon $A'B'C'D'E'F'$ whose opposite sides are still parallel, but all of whose angles are equal to $120°$. Denoting the consecutive sides of $A'B'C'D'E'F'$, starting with side $A'B'$, by a', b', c', d', e', f', it then suffices (because area $A'B'C' = (a'b' \sin 120°)/2$, etc.) to show that

$$a'b' + c'd' + e'f' = f'a' + b'c' + d'e'. \tag{5.4}$$

But (see the figure), $a' = d' + e' - b'$ and $c' = e' + f' - b'$, and when these values for a' and c' are substituted in Eq. (5.4) we obtain an identity. Hence the theorem.

PROBLEMS

5.5-1 Show that the area of an ellipse with semiaxes a and b is πab.

5.5-2 Show that a triangle of maximum area inscribed in an ellipse has its sides parallel to the tangents to the ellipse at the opposite vertices.

5.5-3 Find the maximum area possessed by a triangle inscribed in an ellipse of semiaxes a and b.

5.5-4   Find the minimum area possessed by an ellipse circumscribed about a given triangle of area K.

5.5-5   Prove that if an ellipse is projected orthogonally into a circle, then pairs of perpendicular diameters of the circle correspond to pairs of conjugate diameters of the ellipse. (For a definition of *conjugate diameters* see Problem 5.2-7.)

5.5-6   Prove that the area of any triangle, two of whose sides are conjugate radii of an ellipse, is constant.

5.5-7   Prove that a triangle of maximum area inscribed in an ellipse, and having a fixed chord for base, has its opposite vertex at an extremity of the diameter conjugate to the base.

5.5-8   Construct the maximum triangle which can be inscribed in a given ellipse and which has one of its vertices at a given point on the ellipse.

5.5-9   If PP', QQ' are a pair of variable parallel chords of an ellipse through the two fixed points P and Q on the ellipse, show that $P'Q'$ envelops a concentric homothetic ellipse.

5.5-10 AOB and $A'O'B'$, COD and $C'O'D'$ are pairs of parallel chords of an ellipse. Show that

$$(OA)\,(OB)/(OC)\,(OD) = (O'A')\,(O'B')/(O'C')\,(O'D').$$

5.5-11   We are given two concentric homothetic ellipses. Prove that all chords of the outer one which touch the inner one are bisected by the point of contact.

5.5-12   Show that two parallel tangents to an ellipse are met by any other tangent in points which lie on conjugate diameters.

5.5-13 TP, TQ are tangents, and TRS is a secant, of an ellipse. If V is the midpoint of RS and if QV cuts the ellipse again in U, prove that PU is parallel to TS.

5.5-14   Prove that the greatest ellipse which can be inscribed in a parallelogram touches the parallelogram at the midpoints of the four sides.

5.5-15   Prove that the chord of an ellipse which passes through a fixed point and cuts off the greatest or least area is bisected by the point.

5.5-16   Three congruent homothetic ellipses of semiaxes a and

b are such that each touches the other two externally. Find the area of the curvilinear triangle bounded by the three ellipses.

5.5-17   Using orthogonal projection obtain a generalization of the following theorem: The feet of the perpendiculars dropped from any point of the circumcircle of a triangle on the sides of the triangle are collinear.

5.5 18   Using orthogonal projection obtain a generalization of the following theorem: The center of a circle inscribed in a quadrilateral is collinear with the midpoints of the diagonals of the quadrilateral.

5.5-19   Using orthogonal projection obtain a generalization of the following theorem: If a chord AQ of a circle of radius r cuts the diameter of the circle perpendicular to the diameter through A in point R, then $(AQ)(AR) = 2r^2$.

5.5-20   Prove, without using limits, that if A and A' are the areas of two corresponding triangles under an orthogonal projection, then $A' = A \cos \theta$, where θ is the angle between the planes of the two triangles.

SUGGESTIONS
FOR SOLUTIONS
OF PROBLEMS

1.2-1 Let the quadrilateral be $ABCD$, with $AB = a, BC = b$, $CD = c, DA = d$. Show that $2K = ad \sin A + bc \sin C \leq ad + bc$; similarly, $2K \leq ab + cd$; therefore $4K \leq ad + bc + ab + cd = (a + c)(b + d)$. This formula illustrates the prevalent idea, in early empirical geometry, of averaging.

1.2-2 Take $\pi = 3$.

1.2-8 (a) If r is the radius of the circle, θ half the central angle subtended by the chord, and A the sought area, then $r = (4s^2 + c^2)/8s$, $\theta = \sin^{-1}(c/2r)$, $A = r^2\theta + c(s - r)/2$.

1.2-8 (b) 12 ft.

1.3-1 Set up a vertical stick of length s near the pyramid. Let S_1, P_1 and S_2, P_2 be the points marking the shadows of the top of the stick and the apex of the pyramid at two different times of the day. Then, if x is the sought height of the pyramid, $x = s(P_1 P_2)/(S_1 S_2)$.

1.3-3 A convex polyhedral angle must contain at least three faces, and the sum of its face angles must be less than $360°$.

1.3-5 (a) Suppose that $\sqrt{2} = p/q$, where p and q are relatively prime integers. Then $p^2 = 2q^2$ and it follows that p^2, and hence p, is even. Set $p = 2r$. Then $2r^2 = q^2$ and it follows that q^2, and hence q, is even. This contradicts the hypothesis that p and q are relatively prime.

201

1.3-5   (b)   Suppose that the diagonal d and the side s of a square are commensurable. Then $d = pt$, $s = qt$, where p and q are integers and t is some segment. It follows that $\sqrt{2} = d/s = p/q$, a rational number.

1.3-5   (c)   Suppose that the line passes through the lattice point (q,p) and let m denote the slope of the line. Then $\sqrt{2} = m = p/q$, a rational number.

1.3-7   *Theorem 1.*   Let a be an abba. By P2 there is a dabba A to which a belongs. By P4 there is a dabba B conjugate to dabba A. Since, by P1, B is nonempty, it contains an abba b, and $b \neq a$. By P3 there is a dabba C containing a and b. By P4 there is a dabba D conjugate to dabba C. By P1, D contains an abba c, and $c \neq a$, $c \neq b$. By P3, there is a dabba E containing a and c. Since c belongs to E but not to C, dabbas C and E are distinct. Thus a belongs to two distinct dabbas, C and E.

Theorem 2.   Let A be a dabba. By P1, A contains an abba a. Suppose that a is the only abba in A. By T1, there is a dabba $B \neq A$ and containing a. Now B must contain a second abba $b \neq a$, for otherwise A and B would not be distinct. By P4, there is a dabba C conjugate to dabba B. It follows that A also is conjugate to C. But this contradicts P4. The theorem now follows by *reductio ad absurdum*.

Theorem   3.   In the proof of T1 we showed the existence of at least two distinct abbas a and b. By P3, there is a dabba A to which a and b both belong. By P4, there is a dabba B conjugate to dabba A. But, by T2, B must contain at least two distinct abbas, c and d. Since A and B are conjugate, it follows that a, b, c, d are four distinct abbas.

1.4-5   (b)   See L. S. Shively, *An Introduction to Modern Geometry* (New York: John Wiley & Sons, Inc.), p. 141, or Nathan Altshiller-Court, *College Geometry* (New York: Barnes and Noble, Inc.), pp. 72-73.

1.4-8   (h)   Denote the parts by x and $a - x$. Then $x^2 - (a - x)^2 = x(a - x)$, or $x^2 + ax - a^2 = 0$.

1.5-1   (c) $h_c = b \sin A$.

1.5-1   (f) $h_a = t_a \cos [(B - C)/2]$.

1.5-1   (g) $4h_a{}^2 + (b_a - c_a)^2 = 4m_a{}^2$.

1.5-1   (h) $b_a - c_a = 2R \sin (B - C)$.

1.5-1 (i) $4R(r_a - r) = (r_a - r)^2 + a^2$. If M and N are the midpoints of side BC and arc BC, then $MN = (r_a - r)/2$; clearly any two of R, a, MN determine the third.

1.5-1 (j) $h_a = 2rr_a/(r_a - r)$.

1.5-2 (b) See Problem 3336, *The American Mathematical Monthly*, Aug. 1929.

1.5-2 (c) See Problem E 1447, *The American Mathematical Monthly*, Sept. 1961. The solution given in this reference is a singularly fine application of the method of data.

1.5-3 (b) Let M be the midpoint of BC. The broken line EMA bisects the area. Through M draw MN parallel to AE to cut a side of triangle ABC in N. Then EN is the sought line.

1.5-4 Take the radius of C as one unit and set $p_k = 2k \sin (\pi/k)$, $P_k = 2k \tan (\pi/k)$, $a_k = \frac{1}{2}p_k \cos (\pi/k)$, $A_k = \frac{1}{2}P_k$.

1.5-5 (e) The volume of the segment is equal to the volume of a spherical sector minus the volume of a cone. Also, $a^2 = h(2R - h)$.

1.5-5 (f) The segment is the difference of two segments, each of one base, and having, say, altitudes u and v. Then

$$V = \pi R(u^2 - v^2) - \pi(u^3 - v^3)/3$$
$$= \pi h[(Ru + Rv) - (u^2 + uv + v^2)/3].$$

But $u^2 + uv + v^2 = h^2 + 3uv$, $(2R - u)u = a^2$, $(2R - v)v = b^2$. Hence

$$V = \pi h[(a^2 + b^2)/2 + (u^2 + v^2)/2 - h^2/3 - uv]$$
$$= \pi h[(a^2 + b^2)/2 + h^2/2 + uv - h^2/3 - uv], \text{ etc.}$$

1.5-7 (b) Denote AB by a, AC by b, BC by c, and $\angle ADB$ by θ. Then, by the law of sines, applied first to triangle BCD and then to triangle ABD,

$$\sin 30°/ \sin \theta = a/c, \quad \sin \theta / \sin 120° = a/(b + a).$$

Consequently, $1/\sqrt{3} = \tan 30° = a^2/c(b + a)$. Squaring both sides and recalling that $c^2 = b^2 - a^2$, we find $2a^3(2a + b) = b^3(2a + b)$, or $b^3 = 2a^3$.

1.5-11 (a) From the similar triangles DFB and DBO, $FD/DB = DB/OD$. Therefore $FD = (DB)^2/OD = 2 (AB)(BC)/(AB + BC)$.

1.5-11   (b)   From similar right triangles, $OA/OB = AF/BD = AF/BE = AC/CB = (OC - OA)/(OB - OC)$. Now solve for OC.

1.5-11   (f)   We have $ax \sin 60° + bx \sin 60° = ab \sin 120°$.

1.5-12   For a very neat application of this theorem to the establishment of the Erdös-Mordell inequality: "If P is any point inside or on the perimeter of triangle ABC and if p_a, p_b, p_c are the distances of P from the sides of the triangle, then $PA + PB + PC \geqq 2(p_a + p_b + p_c)$," see N. D. Kazarinoff, *Geometrical Inequalities* (New York: Random House, Inc., 1961), pp. 84–87.

1.5-13   (a) $V = 2\pi^2 r^2 R$, $S = 4\pi^2 rR$.

1.5-13   (b) $2r/\pi$ from the diameter.

1.5-13   (c) $4r/3\pi$ from the diameter.

1.6-1   (a) $x = hd/(2h + d)$.

1.6-1   (b)   8 cubits and 10 cubits.

1.6-1   (c)   20 cubits.

1.6-2   (b)   Since the quadrilateral has an incircle, $a + c = b + d = s$. Therefore $s - a = c, s - b = d, s - c = a, s - d = b$.

1.6-2   (c)   In Fig. S1 we have

$$a^2 + c^2 = r^2 + s^2 + m^2 + n^2 - 2(rn + sm) \cos \theta,$$
$$b^2 + d^2 = r^2 + s^2 + m^2 + n^2 + 2(sn + rm) \cos \theta.$$

Therefore $a^2 + c^2 = b^2 + d^2$ if and only if $\cos \theta = 0$, or $\theta = 90°$.

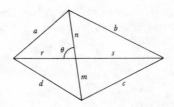

FIG. S1

1.6-2   (d)   Use Problem 1.6-2 (c).

1.6-2   (e)   The consecutive sides of the quadrilateral are 39,

60, 52, 25; the diagonals are 56 and 63; the circumdiameter is 65; the area is 1764.

1.6-4   (a)   Find z such that $b/a = a/z$, then m such that $n/z = a/m$.

1.6-5   (a)   Draw any circle S on the sphere and mark any three points A, B, C on its circumference. On a plane construct a triangle congruent to triangle ABC, find its circumcircle, and thus obtain the radius of S. Construct a right triangle having the radius of S as one leg and the polar chord of S as hypotenuse. It is now easy to find the diameter of the given sphere.

1.6-5   (b)   If d is the diameter of the sphere and e the edge of the inscribed cube, then $e = (d\sqrt{3})/3$, whence e is one-third the altitude of an equilateral triangle of side $2d$.

1.6-5   (c)   If d is the diameter of the sphere and e the edge of the inscribed regular tetrahedron, then $e = (d\sqrt{6})/3$, whence e is the hypotenuse of a right isosceles triangle with the leg equal to the edge of the inscribed cube. See Problem 1.6-5 (b).

1.6-6   (a)   Let the legs, hypotenuse, and area of the triangle be a, b, c, K, $a \geq b$. Then $a^2 + b^2 = c^2$, $ab = 2K$. Solving for a and b we find

$$a = [\sqrt{c^2 + 4K} + \sqrt{c^2 - 4K}]/2, \quad b = [\sqrt{c^2 + 4K} - \sqrt{c^2 - 4K}]/2.$$

1.6-7   (a)   Following is essentially the solution given by Regiomontanus. We are given (see Fig. S2) $p = b - c$, h, $q = m - n$. Now $b^2 - m^2 = h^2 = c^2 - n^2$, or $b^2 - c^2 = m^2 - n^2$, or $b + c = qa/p$. Therefore

$$b = (qa + p^2)/2p \quad \text{and} \quad m = (a + q)/2.$$

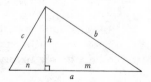

FIG. S2

Substituting these expressions in the relation $b^2 - m^2 = h^2$ yields a quadratic equation in the unknown a.

1.6-7   (b)   Following is essentially the solution given by Regio-montanus. Here we are given (see Fig. S2) $a, h, k = c/b$. Set $2x = m - n$. Then

$$4n^2 = (a - 2x)^2, \quad 4c^2 = 4h^2 + (a - 2x)^2,$$
$$4m^2 = (a + 2x)^2, \quad 4b^2 = 4h^2 + (a + 2x)^2.$$

Then $k^2[4h^2 + (a + 2x)^2] = 4h^2 + (a - 2x)^2$. Solving this quadratic we obtain x, and thence b and c.

1.6-7   (c)   On AD produced (see Fig. S3) take $DE = bc/a$, the fourth proportional to the given segments a, b, c. Then triangles DCE and BAC are similar and $CA/CE = a/c$. Thus C is located as the intersection of two loci, a circle of Apollonius and a circle with center D and radius c.

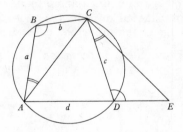

FIG. S3

1.6-8   Using standard notation we have

$$(rs)^2 = s(s - a)(s - b)(s - c),$$

or

$$16s^2 = s(s - 14)(6)(8),$$

and $s = 21$. The required sides are then $21 - 6 = 15$ and $21 - 8 = 13$. This is not Pacioli's method of solving the problem; his solution is needlessly involved.

1.7-1   No, but induction may be employed to conjecture the proposition to which the process is applied.

1.7-2   Fold the vertices onto the incenter of the triangle, or fold the vertices onto the foot of one of the altitudes.

1.7-5   No. Only for so-called *orthocentric tetrahedra* are the four altitudes concurrent. An orthocentric tetrahedron is a tetrahedron each edge of which is perpendicular to the opposite edge.

1.7-6   In the first three cases the binomial coefficients appear. Therefore one might expect the pentatope to have 5 zero-dimensional, 10 one-dimensional, 10 two-dimensional, and 5 three-dimensional bounding elements.

1.7-7   (a)   Parallelepiped, rectangular parallelepiped (box), sphere.

1.7-7   (b)   Prism, right prism, sphere.

1.7-9   Instead of isogonal conjugate lines of a plane angle, consider *isogonal conjugate planes* of a dihedral angle.

1.7-11   The list cannot be continued: there is no convex poly-hedron all of whose faces are hexagons. In fact, it can be shown that any convex polyhedron must have some faces with less than six sides.

1.7-12   (b)   Let D be a point on the surface of P such that the distance CD is a minimum. Show that D can be neither a vertex of P nor lie on an edge of P, and that CD is perpen-dicular to the face F of P on which D lies.

2.1-1   Use Theorem 2.1.3 along with mathematical induction.

2.1-2   Start with $\overline{AM} = \overline{MB}$ and then insert an origin at P.

2.1-3   Start with $\overline{AB} = \overline{OB} - \overline{OA}$ and then square both sides.

2.1-4   Insert an origin at P.

2.1-5   Set $\overline{AA'} = \overline{OA'} - \overline{OA} = (\overline{O'A'} - \overline{O'O}) - \overline{OA}$, etc.

2.1-6   Insert an origin O and let M and N denote the midpoints of CR and PQ. Then $4\overline{OM} = 2\overline{OR} + 2\overline{OC} = \overline{OA} + \overline{OB} + 2\overline{OC} = \overline{OB} + \overline{OC} + 2\overline{OQ} = 2\overline{OP} + 2\overline{OQ} = 4\overline{ON}$. Or, M and N clearly coincide if A, B, C are not collinear; now let C approach collinearity with A and B.

2.1-9   Use Theorem 2.1.9.

2.1-10   Use Theorem 2.1.9.

2.1-11   First consider the case where P is on the line and take P as origin; then let P' be the foot of the perpendicular dropped from P to the line.

2.1-12   Use Stewart's Theorem.

2.1-13   Use Stewart's Theorem.

2.1-14   By Problem 2.1-13, $t_a{}^2 = bc[1 - a^2/(b+c)^2], t_b{}^2 = ca[1 - b^2/(c+a)^2]$. Show that $t_a{}^2 - t_b{}^2 = (a-b)f(a,b,c)$, where $f(a,b,c)$ contains only positive terms.

2.1-15   Use Stewart's Theorem.

2.1-16   (a) Let a line cut OA, OB, OC, OD in A', B', C', D'. Apply Euler's Theorem to A', B', C', D'. Multiply through by p^2, where p is the perpendicular from O onto line $A'B'C'D'$. Replace $p\,\overline{A'B'}$ by $(OA')(OB')\sin\overline{A'OB'}$, etc.

2.1-16   (b) $2\triangle\overline{AOB} = (OA)(OB)\sin\overline{AOB}$, etc. Now use Problem 2.1-16 (a).

2.1-18   Consider three cases: first where O is within triangle ABC, next where O is within $\angle BAC$ but on the other side of BC from A, then where O is within the vertical angle of $\angle BAC$.

2.1-19   Consider the equation where A is replaced by a variable point X on the line. Take any origin O on the line and obtain a quadratic equation in $x = OX$. Take $X = B, C, D$ in turn, obtaining three identities. Then the quadratic equation has three distinct roots, and therefore is an identity. That is, X can be any point on the line, e.g. A.

2.2-2   Each follows from Theorem 2.2.5 or Convention 2.2.4. Thus Theorem (a) becomes: "Through a given point there is one and only one plane containing the ideal line of a given plane not passing through the given point," and this is an immediate consequence of Theorem 2.2.5. Theorem (b) becomes: "Two lines which intersect a third line in its ideal point, intersect each other in their ideal points," and this follows from Convention 2.2.4.

2.2-5   Multiply the identity of Problem 2.1-19 by $\overline{AD}$ and then take D as an ideal point.

2.2-5   Divide the identity of Problem 2.1-19 by $\overline{AQ}$ and then take Q as an ideal point.

2.3-2   (b) Use the trigonometric form of Ceva's Theorem.

2.3-2   (c) Use the trigonometric form of Ceva's Theorem.

2.3-3   Use Ceva's Theorem.

2.3-4   Use Ceva's Theorem.

2.3-5   Use Ceva's Theorem.

2.3-7   Use Menelaus' Theorem.

2.3-8   Use the trigonometric form of Ceva's Theorem.

2.3-9   Use the trigonometric form of Menelaus' Theorem.

2.3-10   Use Ceva's Theorem along with the fact that $(AF)(AF') = (AE)(AE')$, etc.

2.3-11   Let D, E, F be the points of intersection of the tangents at A, B, C with the opposite sides. Then triangles ABD and CAD are similar, and $\overline{BD}/\overline{DC} = -\overline{BD}/\overline{CD} = -(BD)^2/(\overline{BD})(\overline{CD}) = -(BD)^2/(AD)^2 = -c^2/b^2$, etc. Or obtain the result as a special case of Pascal's "mystic-hexagram" theorem, by regarding ABC as a hexagon with two vertices coinciding at A, two at B, and two at C. Or use the fact that, by Problem 2.3-3, the given triangle and the triangle formed by the tangents are copolar.

2.3-12   Use Desargues' two-triangle theorem.

2.3-13   Use the trigonometric form of Menelaus' Theorem.

2.3-14   Use the trigonometric form of Menelaus' Theorem.

2.3-16   Triangles CAC' and $B'AB$ are congruent, whence $\sin ACC'/\sin B'BA = ACC'/\sin CC'A = AC'/CA = AB/CA$, etc.

2.3-18 $\overline{B'D'}/\overline{D'C'} = (OB' \sin \overline{B'OD'})/(OC' \sin \overline{D'OC'})$, etc.

2.3-19   In the figure for Problem 2.3-18 draw a sphere with center O to cut $OA', OB', OC', OD', OE', OF'$ in A, B, C, D, E, F.

2.3-20 $\overline{AA'}/\overline{A'B} = (OA \sin \overline{AOA'})/(OB \sin \overline{A'OB})$, etc.

2.3-21   Apply Menelaus' Theorem to triangles ABC, ACD, ADE, etc.

2.4-4   On a line other than l through C construct A' and B' such that $\overline{CA'}/\overline{CB'} = r$. Let AA' and BB' intersect in D'. Through D' draw the parallel to CB' to intersect l in D.

2.4-5   Let A', B', C', D', P' be the points of contact of the tangents a, b, c, d, p, respectively. Let O be the center of the circle and K any fixed point on the circle. Then $\measuredangle AOP' = \frac{1}{2} \measuredangle A'OP' = \measuredangle A'KP'$, etc. It follows that $(AB,CD) = O(AB,CD) = K(A'B',C'D')$.

2.4-6   Let FA and DC intersect in T, BC and ED in U, BC and FE in V, and AF and DE in R. Consider the four tangents DE, AB, EF, CD. By Problem 2.4-5, $(RA,FT) = (UB,VC)$, whence $D(EA,FC) = D(RA,FT) = E(UB,VC) = E(DB,FC)$. It now follows that DA, EB, FC are concurrent.

2.4-7   (a)   Expand.

2.4-7   (b)   Expand.

2.4-8   Expand and use Menelaus' Theorem.

2.4-9   The proof of Theorem 2.4.12 as given in the text applies here.

2.5-1   (a) $AC/CB = AP/MB = AP/BN = AD/DB$.

2.5-1   (b)   If O is the center of the semicircle, $(\overline{OC})(\overline{OD}) = (OT)^2 = (OB)^2$.

2.5-1   (c)   Apply Theorem 2.3.7.

2.5-2 $(OB)^2 = (OC)(OD) = (O'C - O'O)(O'D - O'O) = (OO' + O'C)(OO' - O'C)$.

2.5-3   (b)   Let AB be the diameter, CD the chord, P a point on the circle. Then $P(AB,CD) = A(TB,CD)$, where AT is the tangent at A. But $A(TB,CD) = (\sin \overline{TAC}/\sin \overline{CAB})/(\sin \overline{TAD}/\sin \overline{DAB})$.

2.5-3   (c) $(AC,LM) = B(AC,LM) = B(AC,DE)$. Now use part (b).

2.5-3   (d)   Use part (b).

2.5-4   (a)   Use Theorem 2.5.3.

2.5-4   (b)   Show that PA bisects $\measuredangle QPR$.

2.5-4   (c)   We have $AU/UT = (AB \cos \tfrac{1}{2}A)/(BT \sin TBU)$ and $AV/VT = (AC \cos \tfrac{1}{2}A)/(TC \sin TCV)$, $AB/AC = BT/TC$, $\measuredangle TBU = \measuredangle TCV$.

2.5-5   Use Problem 2.5-3 (b).

2.5-6   By Theorem 2.1.9 show that $AC/CB = PA/PB = AD/DB$.

2.5-7   Use Theorem 2.5.11 and Problem 2.5-6.

2.5-8   Use the theorems of Ceva and Menelaus.

2.5-9   We have $2/\overline{AB} = 1/\overline{AC} + 1/\overline{AD} = (\overline{AD} + \overline{AC})/(\overline{AC} \cdot \overline{AD}) = 2\overline{AO}/(\overline{AC} \cdot \overline{AD})$.

2.5-10 $(\overline{OP})(\overline{OP'}) = (\overline{OQ})(\overline{OQ'})$, where O is the center of the given circle.

2.5-11 Let AB cut PQ in O. Then O is the midpoint of PQ and $(\overline{OL})(\overline{OM}) = (OQ)^2$.

2.5-12 Let R and r be the radii of the semicircle and Σ respectively. Draw a concentric semicircle of radius $R - r$ and note that r is the geometric mean of $AC - r$ and $CB - r$.

2.5-13 Use Corollary 2.4.8.

2.5-14 $ab = [(a + b)/2][2ab/(a + b)]$.

2.6-2 Use Theorem 2.5.5.

2.6-3 The tangents drawn from the radical center to the three circles are all equal in length.

2.6-5 Use Theorems 2.6.13 and 2.6.14.

2.6-6 The midpoint of a common tangent to two circles has equal powers with respect to the two circles.

2.6-7 P is the radical center of the three circles.

2.6-8 Let the circles have centers O and O' and intersect in P. The circles are orthogonal if and only if triangle OPO' is a right triangle — that is, if and only if $[(c/2)d]/2 = (rr')/2$.

2.6-9 (a) The altitudes are common chords of pairs of the circles.

2.6-9 (b) Let A', B', C' be the feet of the altitudes and H the orthocenter. Then AA', BB', CC' are chords of the three circles and $(\overline{AH})(\overline{HA'}) = (\overline{BH})(\overline{HB'}) = (\overline{CH})(\overline{HC'})$.

2.6-10 (a) Draw the diameter of C_1 through the center of C_2.

2.6-10 (b) Draw the chord of C_1 perpendicular to the diameter of C_1 through P.

2.6-10 (c) Use part (b) and the fact that P has equal powers with respect to the three circles.

2.6-10 (d) If circle $M(m)$ bisects the given circles $A(a)$ and $B(b)$, then $(MA)^2 + a^2 = m^2 = (MB)^2 + b^2$, whence $(MA)^2 - (MB)^2 = b^2 - a^2$.

2.6-10 (e) The center of the given circle has equal powers with respect to all the bisecting circles.

2.6-11   Use Theorem 2.6.13 (1).

2.6-12   (a)   The center of the sought circle is the radical center of the two given circles and the given point.

2.6-12   (b)   If the two given circles are intersecting, use part (a) and Theorem 2.6-18.

2.6-13   Let O be the center of Σ. If A, O, B are collinear, draw the line AOB. If A, O, B are not collinear, draw the circle BAA', where A' is the harmonic conjugate of A with respect to the endpoints of the diameter of Σ passing through A.

2.6-14   Let O be the center of Σ and let line m pass through A and have the given direction. If O lies on m, then m is a straight line orthogonal to Σ. If O does not lie on m, draw the circle whose center is the point of intersection of the perpendicular to m at A and the perpendicular bisector of AA', where A' is the harmonic conjugate of A with respect to the endpoints of the diameter of Σ through A.

3.1-1   (a)   Onto and one-to-one.

3.1-1   (b)   Not onto; 3 is not the image of any element of A.

3.1-1   (c)   Not onto; 2 is not the image of any element of A.

3.1-1   (d)   Not onto; no even integer is the image of any element of A.

3.1-1   (e)   Onto and one-to-one.

3.1-1   (f)   Onto and one-to-one.

3.1-3   Let r' be any real number and let r be a real root of $x^3 - x = r'$. Then $r \to r'$, whence the mapping is onto. The mapping is not one-to-one since $0 \to 0$ and $1 \to 0$.

3.1-4   (b) $n \to (2n + 3)^2, n \to 2n^2 + 3, n \to n^4, n \to 4n + 9, n \to (2n^2 + 3)^2, n \to (2n^2 + 3)^2$.

3.1-7 $S = IS = (T^{-1}T)S = T^{-1}(TS) = T^{-1}I = T^{-1}$.

3.1-8 $T_1^{-1} T_2^{-1} = (T_1^{-1} T_2^{-1})(T_2 T_1)(T_2 T_1)^{-1}$, etc.

3.1-9 $T^{-1}T = I$.   Therefore, by Theorem 3.1.12, $T = (T^{-1})^{-1}$.

3.1-10 $T = T(TT^{-1}) = T^2 T^{-1} = IT^{-1} = T^{-1}$.

3.1-11 $(T_3 T_2 T_1)^{-1} = [(T_3 T_2)T_1]^{-1} = T_1^{-1}(T_3 T_2)^{-1} = T_1^{-1} (T_2^{-1} T_3^{-1}) = T_1^{-1} T_2^{-1} T_3^{-1}$.

3.2-1   (a)   (2,1), (b)   (-1,1), (c)   (1,-1), (d)   (1,-1), (e)   (-1,-1),
(f)   (2,-2), (g)   (4,-2), (h)   (1,½), (i)   (2,-1), (j) (-2,2), (k)   (-2,2),
(l) $(2 - 2\sqrt{2},0)$.

3.2-2   No, for all parts.

3.2-3   If $A = A'$, then $O = A$. If $B = B'$, then $O = B$. If $A \neq A'$,
$B \neq B'$, and AA' is not parallel to BB', then O is the point of
intersection of the perpendicular bisectors of AA' and BB'.
If $A \neq A', B \neq B', AA'$ is parallel to BB', and AB is not
collinear with $A'B'$, then O is the point of intersection of lines
AB and $A'B'$. If AB is collinear with $A'B'$, then O is the common
midpoint of AA' and BB'.

3.2-4   Obvious from a figure.

3.2-5   Place an x axis on BC with origin at the midpoint of BC.

3.2-7   Obvious from a figure.

3.2-8   (a), (b), (c)   Obvious from a figure.

3.3-2   Let a common tangent to circles $A(a)$ and $B(b)$ cut the
line of centers AB in point S. Draw the radii to the points
of contact of the common tangent. Then, from similar triangles, $SA/SB = a/b$, etc.

3.3-3   (a) BD and $B'D'$ are corresponding segments under
the concerned homothety.

3.3-3   (b) $\angle DBA' = \angle DCA = \angle D'C'A'$.

3.3-3   (c)   From the homothety, $SA/SA' = SB/SB'$ and $SC/SC' =
SD/SD'$. Therefore $(SA)(SB') = (SA')(SB)$ and $(SC)(SD') =
(SC')(SD)$. But, by part (b), $(SA')(SB) = (SC')(SD)$.

3.3-3   (d)   Let the two tangents intersect in T. Then $\angle A'BT =
\angle BA'T$, triangle $A'BT$ is isosceles, and T has equal powers
with respect to C_1 and C_2.

3.3-4   Use Theorem 3.3.9.

3.3-5   Use Menelaus' Theorem.

3.3-6   This is a special case of Problem 3.3-5.

3.3-7   Its distance from A is $k^2 c/(k^2 - 1)$, where $k = a/b$.

3.3-8   Let Y_1, Y_2, Y_3 be the images of X_1, X_2, X_3 under the
homothety $H(H,2)$, which carries the nine-point circle into
the circumcircle. Show that triangle $Y_1 Y_2 Y_3$ is equilateral.

3.4-1   Take C not on line AB and let C' be such that triangle $A'B'C'$ is congruent to triangle ABC. There are exactly two possible positions, C'_1 and C'_2, for C', and each position (by Theorem 3.4.2) determines a unique isometry carrying triangle ABC into triangle $A'B'C'$. Since triangles $A'B'C'_1$ and $A'B'C'_2$ can be carried into one another by a reflection in line $A'B'$, it follows that one of the isometries is direct and the other opposite.

3.4-2   A product of three reflections in lines is an opposite isometry, and (by Theorem 3.4.13) an opposite isometry is either a reflection in a line or a glide reflection.

3.4-3   (a), (b)   Use Theorem 3.4.7.

3.4-4   (a)   Use Theorems 3.4.4 and 3.4.5.

3.4-4   (b)   Use Theorem 3.4.13.

3.4-5   (a), (b)   Use Theorems 3.4.11 and 3.4.14.

3.4-6   (a)   By Theorem 3.4.13.

3.4-6   (b)   By Theorem 3.4.14.

3.4-7   (a), (b)   Obvious from a figure.

3.4-8   By Problem 3.4-1 there are exactly two isometries, one direct and one opposite, carrying AB into $A'B'$. If the isometry is opposite, it is (by Theorem 3.4.13) a reflection or a glide-reflection; in either case the midpoints of the segments PP' lie on the axis of the transformation. If the isometry is direct, the result follows from Theorem 3.4.12, the locus degenerating to a point if the isometry is a half-turn.

3.4-9   By Theorem 3.4.13, any opposite isometry is either a reflection in a line or a glide-reflection. If it is a reflection in a line m, choose any line n perpendicular to m and cutting m in the point O. Then $R(m) = R(O)R(n)$. If it is a glide-reflection of vector AB and axis m, choose any line n perpendicular to m cutting m in a point O. Let $\overline{OO'} = \frac{1}{2}\overline{AB}$. Then $G(m,AB) = R(O')R(n)$.

3.4-10   Obvious from a figure.

3.4-11   See Problem 3.4-9.

3.4-12   The maps are related by a nonisometric similarity, or (by Theorems 3.4.11 and 3.4.14) by a homothety or a stretch-reflection.

3.4–13   Use Theorem 3.4.12.

3.6–1   Be careful not to draw more than is asked.

3.6–2   (a)   An intersecting coaxial pencil of circles.

3.6–2   (b)   A tangent coaxial pencil of circles.

3.6–4   (a) $(OC)(OC') = (OB)(2OC)$,   whence $OC' = 2OB$.

3.6–4   (b)   Draw through C the line perpendicular to OC. This line inverts into a circle through O and C' and orthogonal to K'. It follows that O and C' are inverse points relative to circle K'.

3.6–4   (d)   Let orthogonal circles with centers A and B intersect in T, and let M be the midpoint of the common chord. Then $(AM)(AB) = (AT)^2$.

3.6–5   (a)   Let P be any point. Let P' be the inverse of P for circle $A(a)$ and let P'' be the inverse of P' for circle $B(b)$. Let Q be the inverse of P for circle $B(b)$. Now invert the figure with respect to circle $B(b)$. Since circle $A(a)$ inverts into itself (by Theorem 3.5.5) and P and P' are inverse points for circle $A(a)$, it follows (by Theorem 3.6.10) that Q and P'' are also inverse points for circle $A(a)$.

3.6–5   (b)   Invert the figure in circle K_2 and use Theorem 3.6.10.

3.6–6   Invert with respect to D. Then $A'C' + C'B' = A'B'$. But, if p' is the perpendicular distance from D to line $A'B'C'$, we have $A'C'/p' = AC/r$. Similarly, $C'B'/p' = CB/q$, $A'B'/p' = AB/p$. Etc.

3.6–7   Invert the coaxial system into a system of concentric circles, a system of concurrent lines, or a system of parallel lines.

3.6–9   (a)   Such a point is the center of a circle orthogonal to both of the given circles. Invert with respect to this circle.

3.6–9   (b)   When the radical center is outside all three circles.

3.6–10   Use Theorem 3.6.12.

3.6–11   Invert with respect to any point on their radical circle.

3.6–12   Use Theorem 3.6.11 and some circles of Apollonius.

3.6–13   See Problem 3.6–12.

3.6-14 Use Theorem 3.6.10 (2).

3.7-2 Invert with respect to a point on circle C, then use Theorems 2.1.5 and 3.6.11.

3.7-3 Invert with respect to A.

3.7-4 (a) If AB is a diameter of a circle of center O, and if P is a point on the circle, then circles AOP and BOP are orthogonal.

3.7-5 Invert with respect to M.

3.7-6 Invert with respect to T.

3.7-7 Invert with respect to A.

3.7-8 Invert with respect to C.

3.7-9 Use Ptolemy's Theorem.

3.7-10 Subject the figure to the inversion $I(A,1)$.

3.7-11 Invert with respect to D and then apply Stewart's Theorem.

3.7-12 (b) Let C_1 be the circle orthogonal to circle $ABCD$ and passing through A and C; let C_2 be the circle orthogonal to circle $ABCD$ and passing through B and D. Let C_1 and C_2 intersect in X and Y. Invert with respect to X.

3.7-15 We have $OP = (BD)(AO)/AB$. and $OP' = (AC)(OB)/AB$, whence $(OP)(OP') = (BD)(AC)(AO)(OB)/(AB)^2$. But $(BD)(AC) = (AD)^2 - (AB)^2$.

3.8-3 Let O and r be the center and radius of the circle; let Q' be the inverse of Q. Then $(PQ)^2 = (OP)^2 + (OQ)^2 - 2(OQ)(OQ')$ $= (OP)^2 + (OQ)^2 - 2r^2$.

3.8-4 P and Q are inverse points in circle K_2.

3.8-5 Line t is the polar of point T.

3.8-6 (a) Let O be the center of K and let PO cut the polar of P in P'. Now use Theorem 3.5.8.

3.8-6 (b) Use the figure of part (a).

3.8-7 (a) Let Q be diametrically opposite P on circle R. Then (by Problem 3.8-6 (b)) P, Q are conjugate points for K_1, K_2, K_3. Therefore the polars of P for K_1, K_2, K_3 all pass through Q.

3.8-7   (b)   Draw the circle on PQ as diameter. Prove that this circle is orthogonal to the coaxial system. Then use Problem 3.8-6 (b).

3.8-7   (c)   Use part (b).

3.8-7   (d)   Use part (b).

3.8-7   (e)   Use Problem 3.8-6 (a) and (b).

3.8-8   Let P', Q' be the inverses of P, Q. Show that $OP'YQ$ is similar to $OQ'XP$.

3.8-10   (d), (e)   Use part (c).

3.8-10   (f)   The inverse of each vertex of the triangle is the foot of the altitude through that vertex.

3.8-11   (a)   Use Theorem 3.8.12.

3.8-11   (b)   Use part (a) and Problem 3.8-6 (a).

3.8-12   Let ABC and $A'B'C'$ be a pair of conjugate triangles. Let BC and $B'C'$ meet in M and let AA' cut BC in N and $B'C'$ in N'. Then (by Theorem 3.8-10) $(BC,NM) = A'(C'B',MN) = (B'C',N'M)$. It now follows that BB', CC', NN' are concurrent.

3.8-13   Let $A, A'; B, B'; C, C'$ be the three pairs of opposite vertices of the quadrilateral, and suppose $A, A'; B, B'$ are conjugate pairs of points for a circle. Let $A''B''C''$ be the triangle conjugate to triangle ABC. Now $B''C''$ passes through A'. and $A''C''$ passes through B'. But triangles ABC, $A''B''C''$ are copolar (by Problem 3.8-12), and therefore corresponding sides meet in three collinear points, two of which are seen to be A' and B'. It follows that C' must be the third point. That is, $B''A''$ passes through C', and C and C' are conjugate points.

4.1-2   (b)   Let A be the given point and BC be the given line segment. Construct, by Proposition 1, an equilateral triangle ABD. Draw circle $B(C)$, and let DB produced cut this circle in G. Now draw circle $D(G)$ to cut DA produced in L. Then AL is the sought segment.

4.1-3   It is a matter of existence; there exists a greatest triangle inscribed in a circle, but there does not exist a greatest natural number. To complete argument I, we must prove that a maximum triangle inscribed in a circle *exists*. The problem illustrates the importance in mathematics of existence theorems.

4.2-2   First draw a right triangle having the median as hypotenuse and the altitude as a leg.

4.2-3   Locate the center of the circle by the method of loci.

4.2-4   Locate the opposite vertex by the method of loci.

4.2-5   Locate the point as an intersection of some circles of Apollonius.

4.2-6   Let A and B be the positions of the balls, O the center of the circle, and P the point of rebound on the circle. Then PO bisects angle APB. Now use Problem 2.1-9.

4.2-7   Let the given points be A and B and let the required chords be AC and BD. Let E, F be the midpoints of AB, CD; let O be the center of the circle. Then F lies on $O(E)$ and on $E(s/2)$, where $s = AC + BD$.

4.2-8   Locate the center of the sought circle by the method of loci.

4.2-9   Locate the vertex of the angle by the method of loci.

4.2-10   Draw a line parallel to the given line and at a distance from the given line equal to the radius of the given circle. Let P be the foot of the perpendicular from the given point to the drawn circle. Now draw a circle tangent to the parallel at P and passing through the center of the given circle. The sought circle is concentric with this circle.

4.2-11   Translate one circle through a vector determined by the given line segment.

4.2-12   Use Problem 4.2-11.

4.2-13   Reflect one of the curves in the given line.

4.2-14   Use Problem 4.2-13.

4.2-15   Let ABC be the sought triangle and let D, E, F be the given points on the sides BC, CA, AB respectively. Let $\overline{BD}/\overline{DC} = m/n$, $\overline{CE}/\overline{EA} = p/q$, $\overline{AF}/\overline{EB} = r/s$. Find F_1 on line FE such that $\overline{FE}/\overline{EF_1} = q/p$. Next find F_2 on line $F_1 D$ such that $\overline{F_1 D}/\overline{DF_2} = n/m$. Then $F_2 F$ lies along the line AB. Etc.

4.2-16   Take any point D' on BA. Then take E'' on CA such that $CE'' = BD'$. Let circle $D'(B)$ cut the parallel to BC through E'' in E'. Draw a line through E' parallel to AC to cut BA in

A' and BC in C'. We now have a figure homothetic to the desired figure, with B as center of homothety.

4.2-17 Use Problem 4.2-16.

4.2-18 Subject C_2 to the homothety $H(O,k)$, where $k = OP_1/OP_2$.

4.2-19 Use Problem 4.2-18.

4.2-20 Use the method of similitude.

4.2-21 Take any point O on one of the circles and let C_1 and C_2 denote the other two circles. Now use General Problem 4.2.5.

4.2-22 Let $(OP_1)(OP_2) = a^2$. Invert C_2 into C_2' in the circle $O(a)$.

4.2-23 Use Problem 4.2-22.

4.2-24 Invert with respect to the given point.

4.2-26 Increase the radius of each circle by half the distance between two of them, obtaining in this way three circles of which two are externally tangent to one another. Invert with respect to the point of contact of these two circles.

4.3-1 (b) Use successive applications of part (a).

4.3-1 (d) Case 2. Find N on OM such that $ON = n(OM) > (OD)/2$. By Case 1 find N', the inverse of N in $O(D)$. Finally find M' such that $OM' = n(ON')$.

4.3-1 (e) See Problem 3.6-4 (a).

4.3-1 (f) See Problem 3.6-4 (b).

4.3-1 (g) From the points A, B, C, D one can, with a Euclidean compass alone, obtain a circle k whose center is not on AB or $C(D)$. Under inversion in k, line AB and circle $C(D)$ become circles whose centers are constructible (by Problems 4.3-1 (e) and (f)), and points on which are constructible (by Problem 4.3-1 (d)). These circles can then be drawn, and their intersections found. The inverses in k of these intersections are the sought points X and Y.

4.3-1 (h) From the points A, B, C, D one can, with a Euclidean compass alone, obtain a circle k whose center is not on AB or CD. Under inversion in k, lines AB and CD become circles through the center O of inversion. The centers are constructible (by Problems 4.3-1 (e) and (f)), and, since they pass through

O, the circles can be drawn. The inverse in k of the other point of intersection of these circles is the sought point X.

4.3-2 Circle ABC is the inverse of line BC' in circle $A(B)$. Hence use Problem 3.6-4 (a).

4.3-4 We suppose the center O of the circle is given. Draw $A(C)$ and $D(B)$ to intersect in M. Draw $A(OM)$ to cut the given circle in X, Y. Then A, X, D, Y are vertices of an inscribed square. The proof is easy.

4.4-2 Case 1, P not on k. Draw PAB, PCD cutting k in A, B and C, D. Draw AD, BC to intersect in M. Draw AC, BD to intersect in N. Then MN is the sought polar.

Case 2, P on k. Draw any secant m through P and let R and S be any two points on m but not on k. Find the polars r and s of R and S. Then r and s intersect in M, the pole of m. PM is sought polar.

4.4-3 (a) Find, by Problem 4.4-2, the polar p of P, and let p cut k in S and T. Them PS and PT are the sought tangents.

4.4-3 (b) Find the polar p of P by Problem 4.4-2. Or inscribe a hexagon 123456 in k, where $1 \equiv 2 \equiv P$, and use Pascal's mystic hexagram theorem.

4.4-4 (a) Draw (by Problem 4.4.1, page 158) a line m parallel to line ABC. Choose a point V not on m or ABC and let VA, VB, VC cut m in A', B', C'. Let BA' and CB' intersect in V'. Draw $V'C'$ to cut ABC in D; draw DV to cut m in D'; draw $V'D'$ to cut ABC in E; etc.

4.4-4 (b) We illustrate with $n = 5$. In the figure of the solution for part (a), let $A'A$ and $F'B$ intersect in U. Then $B'U$ cuts AB in a point Y such that $AY = (AB)/5$.

4.5-1 If a regular polygon of nine sides can be constructed, then its central angle of $40°$ can be constructed, whence a $60°$ angle can be trisected.

4.5-2 If an angle of $1°$ can be constructed, then so also can an angle of $20°$, whence a $60°$ angle can be trisected.

4.5-3 Let $7\theta = 360°$. Then $\cos 3\theta = \cos 4\theta$ or, setting $x = \cos \theta$, $8x^3 + 4x^2 - 4x - 1 = 0$.

4.5-5 Use the identity of Problem 4.5-4.

4.5-6 Take the diameter of the circle as 1 unit. Then circumference $= \pi$.

4.5-8 Show that BB' and AA' are two mean proportionals between OA and OB. If $OB = 2(OA)$, then $(BB')^3 = 2(OA)^3$. This solution of the duplication problem was given by Apollonius (*ca.* 225 B.C.).

4.5-9 Show that $(AC)^3 = 2(AB)^3$. Essentially this construction for duplicating the cube was given in publications by Viète (1646) and Newton (1728).

4.5-10 Show that $\angle ADB = (1/3) \angle AOB$. This solution of the trisection problem is implied by a theorem given by Archimedes (*ca.* 240 B.C.).

4.5-11 Take $AOB = 90°$ and let M and N be the feet of the perpendiculars from P on OA and OB. Let R be the center of the rectangle $OMPN$. If CD is Philon's line for angle AOB and point P, then $RE = RP$, and hence $RD = RC$. We now have a solution of Problem 4.5-8.

5.1-2 (a) The concerned angles have their corresponding sides parallel.

5.1-2 (b) By part (a).

5.1-3 (a) Denote the required center of perspectivity by V. Then (by Problem 5.1-2 (a)) $\angle AVC = \angle A'B'C' = \alpha$ and $\angle DVF = \angle D'E'F' = \beta$. To find V draw on AC an arc of a circle containing angle α and on DF (on the same side of l) an arc of a circle containing angle β. Since A, C, D, F are in the order A, D, C, F, these arcs must intersect; let X be such an intersection. Now rotate X about line $ADCF$ out of plane π to a position V. Then if we project plane π from center V onto a plane parallel to the plane of V and l the problem is solved.

5.1-3 (b) Not necessarily — only so long as the circular arcs described in the solution of part (a) intersect one another.

5.1-4 Let AB and CD intersect in U, AD and BC in V, AC and BD in W. By Problem 5.1-3 project line UV to infinity and angles VAU and LWM into right angles.

5.1-5 Draw any line cutting the rays of the pencil $U(AB,CD)$ in (ab,cd). Let $U'(A'B',C'D')$ be the projection, under any perspectivity, of the pencil $U(AB,CD)$, and let $(a'b',c'd')$ be the projection of (ab,cd). Then $U(AB,CD) = (ab,cd) = (a'b',c'd') = U'(A'B',C'D')$.

5.1-6   Let V be the center of perspectivity and let X and Y' be the feet of the perpendiculars from V on π and π'. Then the bisectors of $\measuredangle XVY'$ cut π and π' in the isocenters of the perspectivity. Suppose, for example, that the internal bisector of $\measuredangle XVY'$ cuts π and π' in E and E'. Then XE and $E'Y'$ intersect on the axis of perspectivity in a point K, and $EK = E'K$. Let the sides of an angle at E cut the axis of perspectivity in L and M. Then $\measuredangle LEM$ maps into $\measuredangle LE'M$. But triangles LEM and $LE'M$ are congruent. Etc.

5.1-7   The isolines are the reflections of the axis of perspectivity in the vanishing lines of the two planes.

5.1-8   Project $ABB'A$ into a square (by Problem 5.1-4).

5.1-9   The expression is an h-expression.

5.2-1   See Theorem 2.5.4.

5.2-2   Let AB, CT intersect in R. Then the polar of R passes through C and through the harmonic conjugate of R for AB; and hence is CD. Since R is on AB, it follows that CD passes through the pole of AB.

5.2-3   If R is the pole of PQ, then the polar of U is the line through R parallel to AB.

5.2-4 R, S, T lie on the polar of the point of intersection of BC and AD.

5.2-5   (a), (b), (c) The line at infinity touches, intersects, and fails to intersect a parabola, a hyperbola, and an ellipse respectively.

5.2-5   (e)   For the polar of the center of the parallelogram is the line at infinity.

5.2-5   (f)   Let W be the other point of intersection of CT with the conic. Then $(UW,TV) = -1$.

5.2-7   (b)   The diagonals of the quadrilateral formed by the points of contact are diameters (since their poles are at infinity) and hence bisect each other; the quadrilateral is thus a parallelogram. It follows that the poles of the diagonals of the circumscribed parallelogram are at infinity, and these diagonals are then diameters.

5.2-7   (c)   Let P, Q be any two points on the conic and let V be the midpoint of PQ. If C is the center of the conic, CV is the diameter bisecting chords parallel to PQ. Thus CV and PQ are parallel to a pair of conjugate diameters, and are thus perpendicular to one another. Since $PV = VQ$, it follows that $CP = CQ$, and all radii of the conic are equal.

5.2-9   (a), (b)   See Problem 4.4-3.

5.2-11   Apply Carnot's Theorem to triangle ABC; or project into a circle and employ the cross ratios $(BC, A_1 A_2)$ and $(AC, B_1 B_2)$.

5.3-2   A complete quadrilateral.

5.3-3   If lines x, y, u are concurrent and if $x(ab, cu) = y(ab, cu)$, then lines a, b, c are concurrent.

5.3-4 abc is a trilateral, l a fixed line through point ab, o a variable line through point cl. If the join of ao and cb is p and the join of bo and ca is q, then pq and ab determine a fixed line m.

5.3-5   Coaxial triangles are copolar.

5.3-6   If the sides 1, 2, 3, 4, 5, 6 of a hexagon pass alternately through a pair of points, then the three lines p, q, r joining opposite vertices 23 and 56, 45 and 12, 61 and 34 of the hexagon are concurrent.

5.3-7   (a)   A point in the plane of a proper conic lies outside the conic, on the conic, or inside the conic.

5.3-7   (b)   If a variable point on a given line p in the plane of a proper conic c lies outside the conic, the harmonic conjugates of the line with respect to the tangents from the variable point all concur in a point P.

5.3-9   Let P be the pole of p for proper conic c, whose reciprocal is proper conic c'. From an arbitrary point Q of p, external to c, draw the two tangents t, u to c. Denote PQ by q. Then $(pq, tu) = -1$. Now if P', Q', T', U', q', p' are the reciprocals of p, q, t, u, Q, P, then P', Q', T', U' lie on q' and $(P'Q', T'U') = -1$. But T', U' are points of c'. Hence Q' lies on the polar of P' for c'. But Q' lies on p'. Thus p' and the polar of P' with respect to c' both coincide with the locus of Q', and so are identical. It follows that p' is the polar of P' for conic c'.

5.3-10   Use Problem 5.3-9.

5.3-11   (b) $\begin{pmatrix} 10 & 3 \\ 3 & 10 \end{pmatrix}$.

5.4-3   In Fig. 5.4a, choose α so that $\sin \alpha = e(\sin \beta)$.

5.4-4   There are (in general) two spheres tangent to the cone and passing through the given point.

5.4-5   In the notation of Fig. 5.4b, the sum is $2VE_2 - (PF_1 + PF_2)$.

5.5-1   Use Theorems 5.5.2 and 5.5.1 (7).

5.5-2   A maximum triangle in a circle is equilateral.

5.5-3 $(3ab \sqrt{3})/4$.

5.5-4 $(4\pi K \sqrt{3})/9$.

5.5-5   Each of two perpendicular diameters of a circle bisects all chords parallel to the other.

5.5-6   The area of any triangle, two of whose sides are perpendicular radii of a circle, is constant.

5.5-7   Use Problem 5.5-5.

5.5-8   The side opposite the given vertex quadrisects the diameter through the vertex and is parallel to the conjugate diameter.

5.5-9   The corresponding envelope for a circle is seen to be a concentric circle.

5.5-10   Use Theorems 5.5.2 and 5.5.1 (5).

5.5-11   The corresponding theorem for concentric circles holds.

5.5-12   Two parallel tangents to a circle are met by any other tangent in points which lie on perpendicular diameters of the circle.

5.5-13   Orthogonally project the ellipse into a circle, of center O', say. Then the circle $O'T'$ as diameter passes through P', Q', V', whence $\measuredangle T'V'Q' = \measuredangle T'P'Q'$. Etc.

5.5-14   Use Problem 5.5-12.

5.5-16 $ab(\sqrt{3} - \pi/2)$.

5.5-17   Lines drawn from any point on an ellipse parallel to the diameters of the ellipse which bisect the sides of an inscribed triangle cut the respective sides of the triangle in three collinear points.

5.5-19   A chord AQ of an ellipse cuts the diameter of the ellipse conjugate to the diameter through A in point R; CP is the radius of the ellipse parallel to AQ. Then $(AQ)(AR) = 2(CP)^2$.

5.5-20   First consider triangles whose bases lie on the line of intersection of the two planes.

BIBLIOGRAPHY

Altshiller-Court, Nathan, *College Geometry, an Introduction to the Modern Geometry of the Triangle and the Circle*. New York: Barnes & Noble, Inc., 1952.

Coxeter, H. S. M., *Introduction to Geometry*. New York: John Wiley & Sons, Inc., 1961.

———, *Projective Geometry*. New York: Blaisdell Publishing Co., 1964.

Daus, P. M., *College Geometry*. Englewood Cliffs, N. J.: Prentice-Hall, Inc., 1941.

Davis, D. R., *Modern College Geometry*. Reading, Mass.: Addison–Wesley Publishing Co., Inc., 1949.

Eves, Howard, *An Introduction to the History of Mathematics* (second revised ed.). New York: Holt, Rinehart & Winston, Inc., 1969.

———, *A Survey of Geometry, Volume One*. Boston: Allyn and Bacon, Inc., 1963.

———, *A Survey of Geometry, Volume Two*. Boston: Allyn and Bacon, Inc., 1965.

Fishback, W. T., *Projective and Euclidean Geometry*. New York: John Wiley & Sons, Inc., 1962.

Heath, T. L., *The Thirteen Books of Euclid's Elements*, 2nd ed., 3 vols. New York: Cambridge University Press, 1926. Reprinted by Dover Publications, Inc., 1956.

——, *A Manual of Greek Mathematics*. New York: Oxford University Press, 1931.

Jeger, Max, *Transformation Geometry*, trans. by A. W. Deicke and A. G. Howson. London: George Allen and Unwin Ltd., 1966. Original German edition published in 1964.

Kostovskii, A. N., *Geometrical Constructions Using Compasses Only*, trans. by Halina Moss. New York: Blaisdell Publishing Co., 1961. Original Russian edition published in 1959.

Modenov, P. S. and A. S. Parkhomenko, *Geometric Transformations*, 2 vols., trans. by M. B. P. Slater. New York: Academic Press, 1965. Original Russian edition published in 1961.

Pedoe, Daniel, *An Introduction to Projective Geometry*. New York: The Macmillan Company, 1963.

Polya, George., *Mathematical Discovery*, Vol. 1. New York: John Wiley & Sons, Inc., 1962.

Seidenberg, A., *Lectures in Projective Geometry*. Princeton, N. J.: D. Van Nostrand Co., Inc., 1962.

Smogorzhevskii, A. S., *The Ruler in Geometrical Constructions*, trans. by Halina Moss. New York: Blaisdell Publishing Co., 1961. Original Russian edition published in 1957.

Yaglom, I. M., *Geometric Transformations*, trans. by Allen Shields. New York: Random House, Inc., New Mathematical Library, No. 8, 1962. Original Russian edition published in 1955.

Young, J. W. A., ed., *Monographs on Topics of Modern Mathematics Relevant to the Elementary Field*. New York: Longmans, Green and Company, 1911. Reprinted by Dover Publications, Inc., 1955.

INDEX